CONTENTS

6 **Story 1:** A Meeting of Two Journeys

12 Pokémon Quiz Part 1

14 Pokémon Scramble

15 Pokémon Sudoku

16 Thunderbolt Code

18 **Story 2:** An Explosive Operation!

24 Pokémon Quiz Part 2

26 Criss-Cross Pokémon

27 Poké Ball Search

28 Search and Find

33 A to Z of Pokémon

78 Answers

WELCOME POKÉMON TRAINER!

Inside the pages of this 2017 Pokémon Annual we will take you on a journey through the region of Kalos, where Ash and his friends Serena, Bonnie and Clemont are learning about Pokémon then battling them against the Trainers that they meet along the road to Snowbelle City. Ash is preparing for his eighth Pokémon Gym Battle, while Team Flare has plans for a new Legendary Pokémon called Zygarde, with Team Rocket getting in the way as usual.

Read the stories of how Ash got to battle against a Mega Charizard with his Greninja, and what happened when Team Rocket came face to face with Team Flare in a battle for a brand new Pokémon. We have activity pages packed with puzzles, quizzes and brain teasers to test your Pokémon knowledge too - have you got what it takes to be a Pokémon Master?

Expand your Pokémon brainboxes with our Pokédex of **771** Pokémon - it's full of information and stats on all of your favourites, so you will have all the Pokémon knowledge to hand when you take part in your next Pokémon Battle. Inside our Pokédex you will find Mythical Pokémon that are so rare people doubt they even exist; Legendary Pokémon that are super-powerful and feature in the myths and legends of the Pokémon world; and Mega Pokémon that have evolved to their Mega state by holding a Mega Stone while their Trainer holds a Key Stone.

Have fun, and remember...
Gotta Catch 'Em All!™

A MEETING OF TWO JOURNEYS!

A battle with an old friend leads to meeting a new one...

It's a beautiful day on the path to Snowbelle City as we catch up with Ash Ketchum, his trusty Pokémon Pikachu and their friends. It may be chilly in the Kalos region, but today the sky is a deep blue with wisps of white cloud floating by. Having crossed paths with his friend Sawyer, the two Pokémon Trainers decide to have a battle to see how each other's skills have improved, watched by Serena, Bonnie and Clemont.

Ash chooses to battle with a Hawlucha, a Fighting-and Flying-type Pokémon, while Sawyer brings out his Dragon-type Pokémon Shelgon. The battle doesn't last long, Ash's Hawlucha is soon triumphant.

"There's no doubt you're strong, Ash," says Sawyer, "But I'm gonna win the next one!" The two friends decide that a Best of Three Pokémon Battle is just what they need.

Sawyer brings out a new Pokémon, Honedge the Steel-and Ghost-type Pokémon. The Pokédex reminds everyone it is said that Honedge is actually a spirit living inside a sword.

"So you caught a new Pokémon, huh?" exclaims Ash, as he turns to his trusty Pikachu for this battle. "Pikachu, Iron Tail!" he shouts to the Electric-type Pokémon. Ash and Pikachu have won so many battles together. Sawyer counters the Iron Tail move with a Fury Cutter, but Pikachu quickly follows up with his Thunderbolt. The battle is soon over, Honedge unable to continue.

All this time, Alain, who is studying Mega Evolution in Pokémon, has been watching from a distance.

With a press of his Poké Ball, Sawyer releases Sceptile, the Grass-type forest Pokémon with seeds on its back that are full of vitamins; Ash brings out his third Pokémon Greninja, a Water and Dark-type ninja Pokémon.

Sawyer picks Bullet Seed as Sceptile's first move, with Ash commanding Greninja to use Water Shuriken. The two Pokémon bash heads as they throw special moves to and fro.

"Can you go on Greninja?" exclaims Ash.

Sawyer yells, "I'm pretty sure I've figured out Greninja's battling style. It uses speed to get up close so it can finish up the battle with just one attack." He then decides to attack from a distance to have the advantage.

Ash is concerned for his Greninja, but feels there's no doubt he can win. "Greninja, let's do this! Use Aerial Ace!" This sends Sceptile flying back and the match goes to Ash.

Sawyer moans, "No matter what I try I can't keep up with you Ash." The battle seems to wipe out Ash making him tired. He tells Sawyer he doesn't really know how he does it, things just flash in front of his eyes.

After a trip to Nurse Joy at a nearby Pokémon Center, everyone is feeling fine again. Ash notices a mysterious stranger arrive and deposit a Poké Ball, this is Alain who was watching the Trainers battle earlier on the path. The friends talk about what it's like to be in a Pokémon Battle.

"It's really hard to explain," says Ash, "I guess it's like all the things that Greninja's seeing and doing, I'm seeing and doing the exact same things at the same time." Everyone is shocked as Ash continues, "Then I start to burn up! Like I'm on fire! After that, I wanna go to sleep."

"It sounds to me like you turn into Greninja," exclaims Sawyer.

Ash loves the idea, "I become Greninja? That would be kind of cool if it was true…"

The conversation between the Pokémon battling friends is being watched by Team Rocket through special binoculars. James, Jessie, Meowth and Wobbuffet are desperate to find out Ash's secrets. The friends talk about how the bond between Trainer and Pokémon becomes stronger as they battle together. In a strange way, that could be what is happening to Ash.

Alain calls Lysandre Labs to check on his Pokémon. "Alain? As the data I sent to you earlier shows, the Mega Evolution energy has accumulated according to plan."

"Thank you, Lysandre," Alain replies, before asking, "I was wondering how Mairin and Chespin are doing."

"Still the same. No change for either of them." Lysandre confirms. Alain pledges to keep on fighting until Chespin recovers and Mairin can smile again.

Sawyer is off home, leaving Ash with Serena, Clemont and Bonnie.

"Ash, let's battle again soon!" he says, having enjoyed his Pokémon battle experience. In the distance Alain glances over at the friends.

On a dark island far out in the ocean, heavy machinery is pulled into place by a laboratory control room full of bald-headed goons in safety glasses. "Now, all of you please behave," it's Xerosic, one of the scientists from Team Flare. He and his laboratory are readying an experiment.

"Firing energy" says a lab technician, pressing a big button. Small green creatures behind glass start to glow while the readings on the lab screens flutter. The lab team quickly move to the next stage, firing a beam of green energy out across the nearby countryside. They all look on shocked as a mushroom cloud erupts in the distance.

Xerosic is overjoyed, "Such a remarkable reaction with only ten Cells. Simply wonderful!" But what have they just done?

Ash and his friends are fast asleep when a giant hand on the end of a long robotic arm smashes through the wall and grabs Pikachu, pulling the Electric-type Pokémon from its bed and into the fresh air.

"Pikachu!" shouts Ash, leaping out of bed and following his number one Pokémon. It turns out the robotic arm belongs to Team Rocket, floating above the house the friends were sleeping in, in a giant Meowth balloon with mechanic arms.

"Rise and shine, losers!" Jessie, James and Meowth all shout together.

"What are you doing here?!" Ash yells back, but they are making their getaway with his precious Pikachu. Team Rocket blast off! Not even Ash commanding Pikachu to do a Thunderbolt move is enough to stop them.

Ash leaps from the window and gives chase, but Team Rocket are ready for him.

"You twerps need your beauty sleep!" exclaims Jessie, and sends an Inkay and Gourgeist flying from their Poké Balls. Inkay goes into a Psybeam move while Gourgeist does a Shadow Ball, scattering Ash as he leaps out of the way of the powerful moves.

Ash is worried for his friends, but as he asks if they're OK, another barrage of moves come his way...

"Now Gourgeist, Dark Pulse!" shouts Jessie, and black and purple pulses of energy fire towards the unprotected Ash. Somehow it seems that Ash has blocked the move. Team Rocket look on in shock.

As the dust clears, we discover that Ash didn't block the move at all. It was a Charizard, under the control of Alain that saved Ash.

"Who are you? Keep your flames out of our fight!" shouts Jessie, but Alain isn't listening.

"Charizard! Use Dragon Claw!" commands Alain, and the large Pokémon dives towards the Team Rocket balloon, slicing one of the robotic arms off in one swoop.

Pikachu falls to the ground out of control until Ash commands, "Pikachu! Use Thunderbolt!" The Electric-type Pokémon sends a crackle of electricity from his cheeks, snapping and sparking around the Team Rocket balloon. Alain tells Charizard to catch Pikachu, and the flame Pokémon majestically soars through the sky to grab Pikachu before it hits the ground. Meanwhile, with the balloon exploding around them, Team Rocket is left flying through the air, wondering where they went wrong.

Pikachu returns to Ash's shoulder and Alain congratulates his Pokémon, "Well done, Charizard." Alain tells Ash that he is impressed by his Pokémon skills, firing a Thunderbolt while falling to the ground is a tricky thing to pull off.

"But if Charizard hadn't been there, it wouldn't have worked. Thanks a lot, Charizard," replies Ash, grateful for the large Pokémon's help. Ash spots that Alain's Charizard has a large stone hanging around its neck.

"Is that a Mega Stone? That means Charizard is able to..." but Ash doesn't get to finish...

"Care to see?" says Alain, "How about a battle between my Charizard and your Greninja? I saw you battle yesterday. I'd like to see more of that."

"That'd be great. Let's go for it!" replies Ash. And with that, the two Pokémon Trainers release Pokémon from their Poké Balls and Clemont steps up to be the referee of the one-on-one Pokémon battle.

"I'll go first!" commands Ash, "Water Shuriken!" and with that, Greninja sends a blast of spinning shurikens out towards Charizard.

"Use Dragon Claw!" commands Alain, with the flame Pokémon easily slicing the shuriken into pieces as the friends look on in disbelief. Thinking that this was a sneaky move, Alain reminds himself that he can do better than that.

"Now, Greninja, use Cut!" shouts Ash, and Charizard dodges left and right to avoid the slicing moves raining down.

"Use Flamethrower!" exclaims Alain, and Charizard fires a wall of flames towards the unsuspecting Greninja, barbecuing the Pokémon in mid-air and weakening it.

With Greninja weak, Alain is ready to impress, pressing a button on the bracelet he is wearing. "Now respond to my heart, Key Stone!" he says, "Beyond Evolution! Mega Evolve!" and Charizard starts to morph, lightning crackling around its Mega Stone. The orange flame Pokémon becomes its Mega Evolved version with toughened claws that deliver much more powerful moves. The friends are amazed to see a black Charizard.

"Wow, wow, wow!" exclaims Bonnie, but Ash isn't scared.

"Now I'm really fired up! We can win this, right Greninja?" and the ninja Pokémon grunts in agreement.

Alain sends out a Dragon Claw from Mega Charizard, while Ash responds with a Cut from Greninja. The two moves smash into each other in a flash of energy, cancelling each other out. "Double Team!" shouts Ash, and multiple Greninja start to appear all over the sky. The move is an illusion, but enough to confuse a competitor.

"Flamethrower!" shouts Alain, and Mega Charizard shoots down the false Greninja.

"Use Aerial Ace!" responds Ash, with Alain sending out a Thunder Punch in retaliation. Clemont and Ash are surprised that the Thunder Punch from Mega Charizard is electric, with the sizzling Greninja suffering from the move.

"All right... hurry up then show me. Thunder Punch, one more time!" exclaims Alain, and Ash's ninja Pokémon screams for mercy.
Greninja is not done though, "I think it's time to show them what we can do!" Ash says, trying to motivate his Pokémon one last time. As Ash and Greninja's eyes meet, they form a bond that fuses them as one.

"It seems like Mega Evolution... but they're not using the stones. Is their bond that strong?" wonders Alain. Ash commands the rejuvenated Greninja to use Aerial Ace, while the Mega Charizard takes to the air. The two Pokémon slam into each other with incredible force. One releasing a Thunder Punch, the other a Cut.

Seizing his moment, Alain shouts, "Blast Burn!" and the Mega Charizard gives an incredible burst of energy, sending clouds of smoke into the air. As the dust clears, a defeated Greninja lies on the ground, completely stunned. Charizard is declared the winner.

Ash introduces himself to Alain with a handshake, both of the Pokémon Trainers agreeing that it was a great battle. What neither of them realise is that their meeting will be an important moment for the future of the Kalos region.

POKÉMON QUIZ

Part 1

Have you been reading carefully? Let's see how well you do in the Pokémon Quiz. The questions are based on the story in this annual, 'A Meeting of Two Journeys!', so you can read first to refresh your memory if you like!

How much do you know about Ash's adventures in the Kalos region?

With Pikachu on his shoulder, Ash is adventuring through the Kalos region with his friends Bonnie, Clemont and Serena when they come across a Mega Evolution Trainer called Alain. What can they find out about the transformation of Ash's Greninja, and just what is the significance of the Legendary Pokémon Zygarde?

1

Ash is battling with an old friend, Sawyer, at the start of the story. Which Pokémon does Ash choose first?

A. Pikachu   **B.** Pidgeot   **C.** Hawlucha

2

As Ash and his friend battle on the pathway to Snowbelle City, someone is watching from a distance, but who?

A. Alain   **B.** Brock   **C.** Nurse Joy

3

Sawyer wants to impress Ash with his Honedge Pokémon, it is said that this Pokémon is a spirit living inside a what?

A. Chesse   **B.** Box   **C.** Sword

4

When Ash battles with Greninja, what is it like for him?

A. Like he's seeing double
B. Like he's on fire
C. Like he's back home in Pallet Town

5

In the laboratory, scientists are working with green creatures - which organisation do they work for?

A. Team Flare
B. Team Rocket
C. Team Pokémon

6

Team Rocket try to steal Pikachu from right under Ash's nose. How do they get about?

A. Jet plane
B. Helicopter
C. Balloon

7

Which move is Ash and Pikachu's favourite to get themselves out of trouble?

A. Thunderbolt   B. Tackle   C. Razor Leaf

8

What does Alain's Charizard wear around its neck?

A. A garland of flowers
B. A sparkly necklace
C. A Mega Stone

9

What Pokémon does Charizard evolve into when battling against Ash's Greninja?

A. Super Charizard
B. Mega Charizard
C. Maxi Charizard

10

Ash and Alain meeting will become an important event for the future of which region?

A. Kanto   B. Johto   C. Kalos

Answers on Page 78!

What kind of Trainer are you?

If you scored 0-2 = **Beginner**
If you scored 3-6 = **Learning**

If you scored 7-9 = **Ace**
If you scored 10 = **Pokémon Master**

POKÉMON SCRAMBLE!

Can you unscramble the letters to find the names of people and Pokémon hidden in this puzzle? Everyone here is in the Pokémon episode 'A Meeting of Two Journeys!', you can read the story on page 6 to give yourself a helping hand.

Once you have worked out the names, put the letters in the correct order in the boxes, then take the circled letters and unscramble them to find a Pokémon dear to Ash.

NOINEB ☐☐☐☐⊙☐

TEPCILSE ☐☐☐⊙☐☐☐☐

ERJYUSON ☐⊙☐☐☐☐☐☐

TEOMWH ☐☐☐☐☐⊙

DAYSENLR ☐☐☐⊙☐☐☐☐

XORCESI ☐☐☐☐☐☐⊙

NIAYK ☐☐⊙☐☐

THE SECRET POKÉMON IS ⊙⊙⊙⊙⊙⊙⊙

14

Pokémon Sudoku

Time to test your Pokémon drawing skills and brainbox logic at the same time!

These Pokémon Sudoku puzzles are made up of 16 squares, split into four blocks of four. Each block of four squares must have one of each Pokémon in it, but the tricky part is that each line from top to bottom, and each line from left to right must also have one of each Pokémon in it.

Draw the Pokémon into the squares when you have worked out which one goes where!

Puzzle 1

(Pikachu)	white	orange	(Pokémon)
(Charizard)	blue	(Pikachu)	white
while	orange	blue	(Pikachu)
blue	yellow	(Meowth)	orange

Puzzle 2

black	(Chespin)	blue	green
(Honedge)	(Sceptile)	black	brown
brown	blue	(Sceptile)	black
(Sceptile)	(Pancham)	(Chespin)	(Honedge)

Puzzle 3

(Shelmet)	blue	(Litten)	brown
grey	(Dedenne)	(Pokémon)	pink
(Pokémon)	(Shelmet)	brown	grey
(Dedenne)	grey	pink	(Pokémon)

Puzzle 4

green	(Skorupi)	(Noibat)	brown
brown	yellow	green	(Skorupi)
yellow	(Pokémon)	purple	green
(Skorupi)	(Pokémon)	(Pokémon)	yellow

THUNDERBOLT CODE

One of Pikachu's favourite special moves is the Thunderbolt - a move used by Electric-type Pokémon that is capable of generating 100,000 Volts! Pikachu has unleashed a Thunderbolt on the grid on the right, sending sparks rattling through, but stopping on squares in the grid. Can you compare the Thunderbolt grid to the letter grid, work out the secret code and decipher the phrase?

WHEN many PIKACHU GATHER THEIR ELECTRICITY CAN build and can cause lightning storms

AN EXPLOSIVE OPERATION!

Two teams battle to capture one Pokémon...

With the sun streaming down through the trees and water babbling by in the river, Ash, Pikachu and Dedenne are lying back in a shady nook, enjoying a well earned rest before Ash heads for Snowbelle City and his eighth Gym battle. Bonnie is playing with a little green creature she calls Squishy. Squishy is not recognisable as a Pokémon, not appearing in any Pokédex. It feeds on sunlight and is in fact a Core Zygarde.

Loving everything cute, Bonnie starts to sing to Squishy...

"Squishy and me... nuzzling cheeks, Best friends forever... we're so happy I promise I'll never... Leave Squishy... sweet little Squishy, Here's my song for you, my sweet Squishy... that's you!"

What the friends don't realise is that they are all being watched from the shadows. Team Rocket has a special cube computer that puts them in touch with their boss Giovanni at headquarters.

"Sir! There's something you need to know of the utmost importance!" says Jessie, jumping at the sight of her superior.

"That's right! There is an evil organisation that stands in Team Rocket's way of conquering the world, and they're located here in Kalos," adds James. Describing the red outfits and sunglasses, Giovanni knows straight away who are they talking about.

Meowth chips in, "They're after a certain kind of Pokémon, which is brand new!" He shows the boss pictures of a green creature... it looks like Bonnie's Squishy!

"Then catch it. You must catch it before they do," commands Giovanni. So Team Rocket set off on a mission in their Meowth balloon to find this mysterious organisation, hoping for a big pat on the back from their boss.

Back by the riverside, Pancham and Chespin want to play with Squishy, who seems more interested in sleeping. The little green creature hops over the rocks in the river to find a more secluded spot, but when it tries to sleep it seems to have nightmares of a more scary time.

A Dragon-type Druddigon Pokémon explodes from the ground, roars and chases the little creature... until it is snapped out of its bad dream by Bonnie, who wonders why it is so sad. Perhaps another one of her Squishy songs will cheer it up?

Settling back down to sleep to Bonnie's lullaby, Squishy is right back in its nightmare. What Squishy is seeing is one of his friends, known as Z2, being captured nearby. It turns out that Mable and Aliana from Team Flare are out to catch the little green creature, confronting it in a canyon. In a desperate bid to escape, Z2 attempts to camouflage itself. It works at first, but a laser beam from Mable puts a stop to that.

"This is Mable. Doctor, the beam is very effective," she tells Xerosic from Team Flare who is back at headquarters.

"Of course! The beam's my invention, after all. Mega Evolution energy is proving how useful it is once again," boasts the scientist.

"All right, time to go," says Mable as she reaches for Z2, but the little creature has other ideas, leaping into the air in a bid to escape. Aliana commands Druddigon to use Slash on the tiny creature, then Mable commands Weavile to attack too. Defending itself, Z2 performs a special move that sucks in green Cell energy from all around, becoming more powerful with every second that passes. With an explosion, the tiny Z2 transforms into the Pokémon Zygarde, in its 10% dog-like Forme.

The newly formed Zygade starts attacking the Druddigon, while Xerosic watches excitedly from back at headquarters. Mable and Aliana command their Pokémon to attack, "Use Dragon Pulse!" screams Aliana to Druddigon.

"Use Metal Claw!" screams Aliana to Weavile, while the entire Team Flare force open fire on the new Pokémon. But none of them are a match for the might of Zygarde and the new Pokémon sends a purple blast of energy rippling through the canyon.

"What do you think you're doing?! This is our chance to catch it, while the beam is still affecting it!" exclaims Xerosic.

"Understood," replies Mable, and the battle goes on.

Team Rocket are strolling through the trees of Kalos, looking for the people they have nicknamed 'the eyewear gang', but having no luck finding them. Then James stumbles upon a little creature, "Squishy?" they all wonder together. "No, its markings are different. Perhaps a Squishy of a different colour?" says James.

Thinking they have come across a rare Squishy, the team attempt to capture it, but Squishy has other ideas. It sends out a flash of energy that freezes the gang on the spot. When they smash their icy covering to break free, Team Flare has arrived. "The glasses gang returns!" exclaims James.

"Here we go. Who are you?" barks Mable, while Jessie and James reply with a Team Rocket motto...

"Prepare for trouble. Here we go, indeed.
And make it double as you recede.
To protect the world from devastation!
To unite all people within our nation!
Those gaudy glasses are a complete waste!
The one thing you lack is: taste!
It's Jessie, and it's James!
Team Rocket blasts off with clear 20/20 vision!
Surrendering now would be a most prudent decision!"

Team Flare hasn't got time for the foolish antics of Team Rocket, and simply get out their blaster guns, firing at Z2. Team Rocket leap into the beam to protect their Pokémon prize, sending out Inkay to retaliate with a Psybeam. It does the trick, stopping the blast. Mable sends out Druddigon again, "Use Metal Claw!" she commands.

Jessie releases her Pokémon, "All right, Gourgeist, use Seed Bomb!" The Pokémon attack each other as the dust clouds build. When the dust settles, Team Rocket and Squishy have gone, leaving Mable to explain to Xerosic that they have failed to capture Z2.

Searching for someone nearby who could help Team Flare out, Xerosic turns to Lysandre, "There is someone, but this person is your..." but we don't find out who it is!

Deep in a dark canyon Team Rocket has been running to escape from Team Flare, they have Squishy with them. The little green creature seems to be in pain, but then Meowth remembers that Squishys need sunshine to get their energy - they are all in the dark. "Time for some tanning," says James, and they set off to find a good spot for sunbathing.

Placing the little creature into direct sunlight, James can see the greenness return to its skin, "Success. You're green with health!" As Jessie and Meowth rejoice that the boss will be pleased, an Ice Beam hits Jessie, turning her hand into an ice cube. It's Team Flare, they have tracked them down.

Team Flare want to battle, sending out Weavile with a Metal Claw move, each team is desperate to get Squishy back to their headquarters. Team Rocket don't hang around for a battle, they are already running in the opposite direction. Giving chase, Weavile's move blasts Team Rocket out of hiding. Aliana commands Druddigon to perform Dragon Pulse, but Wobbuffet is quick to respond, performing its Mirror Coat move that gives double damage.

Out of the dust cloud a Poochyena, Sneasel, Skorupi and Druddigon all dash towards Team Rocket while Weavile leaps into the air and performs an Icy Wind move, sending the team cowering for cover from the cold blast. As Team Flare prepare to retrieve Z2, Jessie sends out her Gourgeist with a Dark Pulse move.

It's a battle between Gourgeist and Weavile with Metal Claw going up against the Dark Pulse, then Inkay gets involved with a Psybeam and Druddigon is back with Slash. All of this battling over one tiny green creature.

Jessie screams a command, "Gourgeist, Leech Seed, let's go!" sending a root rumbling along the canyon floor, up and around the unsuspecting Druddigon, tightening around the Dragon-type Pokémon's chest. Weavile's Metal Claw slashes the root to pieces and everyone in Team Flare attack at once.

Z2 has had enough of the rival Teams battling over it, and starts to suck in green Cell energy from all around, like it did before. This time, as the energy is absorbed by the tiny green creature it evolves into Zygarde 50%, taking the shape of a green and black snake-like Pokémon with hexagonal eyes.

"What is that thing?" screams Jessie.

"Oh boy…" Aliana yells into the chaos, "it's really mad…"

The Zygarde knows how to stop both teams attacking it and performs a Dragon Pulse, sending both Team Flare, Team Rocket and all of their Pokémon flying in all directions.

As the dust clears, Zygarde 50% is left standing in a giant crater. "That power… it's the real deal!" exclaims Aliana.

"This is not going to end the same as it did in Terminus Cave!" adds Mable, and as Druddigon and Weavile square up to Zygarde, the powerful Pokémon starts another Dragon Pulse.

"Oh no. Not again!" exclaims Aliana, but before Zygarde can release its special move, a Flamethrower move blasts into it - it's Charizard.

"Just in the nick of time!" says Xerosic back at the Team Flare HQ. It's Alain and his Charizard, brought in by Xerosic to help out Team Flare. Team Rocket recognise the Charizard too.

"I'll buy you some time. Be ready," Alain tells Mable and Aliana, "Now, Charizard! Use Dragon Claw!" As he steps out into the open, Team Rocket recognise Alain too.

This is no basic Charizard, Alain commands his Pokémon to Mega Evolve, "Respond to my heart, Key Stone! Beyond Evolution! Mega Evolve!" This has now become a colossal battle between Zygarde 50% and Mega Charizard X! "Quick! Block its attack!" Alain yells at the new black Charizard. The new Mega-Evolved Pokémon charge headlong into each other sending pulse waves of energy blasting out. Team Flare use their blaster beams on Zygarde too, still hoping to capture the creature.

Mega Charizard X is sent smashing into the canyon walls over and over again and Zygarde appears to increase in power with each blast. "Guess it won't be as easy to defeat as I hoped," says Allain as he wonders how to approach the battle next.

With Zygard 50% growing, Mable commands Team Flare to use full power and multiple beams fire into the creature at once, returning it to the size of Squishy again. "That little tyke belongs to us!" James exclaims, as Mable produces a box to capture the creature in, but Weavile and Druddigon soon put a stop to Team Rocket's actions, sending them flying into the air once more.

"We're blasting off again!" shout Team Rocket, and then they are gone.

Placing Z2 into the box, Mable confirms to Xerosic that the creature is theirs, "Yes! We finally succeeded!" he declares. Alain congratulates Charizard on a good job.

Turning to Alain, Mable says, "Thanks to you, we completed our mission successfully."

But Aliana is not so complementary, "Why the help? You answer to Lysandre and Lysandre alone!"

"He gave me a direct order. And that was to catch Z2," replied Alain.

Meanwhile, Team Rocket have to explain to their boss Giovanni that they let Squishy fall through their fingers. They tell him about the new species that transforms into an incredibly powerful Pokémon, then the branch they are lying on snaps and they all fall to the ground.

Back by the riverside, Bonnie's Squishy is still looking sad, unable to get any response from the other Squishy it could detect nearby. Bonnie picks it up to comfort it.

Team Flare has advanced their operation and the wheels of fate have begun to turn, Lysandre has claimed Zygarde for himself, drawing the Kalos region ever closer to devastation.

POKÉMON QUIZ
Part 2

Have you been reading carefully? Let's see how well you do in the Pokémon Quiz. The questions are based on the story in this annual, 'An Explosive Operation!', so you can read first to refresh your memory if you like!

How much do you know about Ash's adventures in the Kalos region?

While Ash and his pals rest in a wooded glade, a battle is raging nearby with the prize to capture a mysterious creature. Pokémon, special moves and beams from laser guns are not enough to bring this new Pokémon under control.

1

Ash is resting as he will soon be taking part in a Gym battle in Snowbelle City. Which battle is this?

A. Gym battle 7   **B.** Gym battle 8   **C.** Gym battle 9

2

Bonnie has a new pet that she loves very much and sings to it. What has she called it?

A. Fishy   **B.** Squashy   **C.** Squishy

3

What is the name of the boss at Team Rocket headquarters that James, Jessie and Meowth are so keen to impress?

A. Giovanni   **B.** Ginnelli   **C.** Jem

4

What does Bonnie's little green creature like to do most in the world?

A. Dance   **B.** Sleep   **C.** Eat poffin

5

Who invented the laser beam that can capture Z2 by stopping it camouflaging itself?

A. Xerosic   **B.** Lysandre   **C.** Alain

6

Using green Cell energy, Z2 can transform itself into a Zygarde Pokémon. Which Forme does it take first?

A. Dog   **B.** Snake   **C.** Panda

7

What nickname do Team Rocket give Team Flare?

A. The Red Hand Gang
B. The Bloodhound Gang
C. The Eyewear Gang

8

With both teams failing to capture Z2, back at Team Flare headquarters Xerosic has someone in mind who could help, who is it?

A. Ash   **B.** Alain   **C.** Brock

9

The second time Z2 absorbs green Cell energy from all around, what Forme does it take?

A. Dog   **B.** Cow   **C.** Snake

10

With an all-powerful Zygarde too much for Team Rocket or Team Flare, which Pokémon is the only one that can defeat it?

A. Mega Charizard X
B. Mega Blaziken
C. Pikachu

Answers on Page 78!

What kind of Trainer are you?

If you scored 0-2 = **Beginner**
If you scored 3-6 = **Learning**

If you scored 7-9 = **Ace**
If you scored 10 = **Pokémon Master**

CRISS CROSS

Pokémon

We have filled this criss-cross puzzle with 20 of the characters from the Pokémon story `An Explosive Operation!' - both people and Pokémon!
There are no clues to the whereabouts of each of the names, but we have filled in a few spaces for you. See if you can slot the names into the squares to complete the puzzle.

1 ALIANA	6 DRUDDIGON	11 JESSIE	16 TEAMFLARE
2 ASH	7 GIOVANNI	12 MABLE	17 TEAMROCKET
3 BONNIE	8 GOURGEIST	13 MEOWTH	18 WEAVILE
4 CHARIZARD	9 INKAY	14 PIKACHU	19 XEROSIC
5 CHESPIN	10 JAMES	15 SQUISHY	20 ZYGARDE

POKÉ BALL SEARCH

There are 22 Pokémon trapped inside this Poké Ball, can you find all of their names which could be running horizontally, vertically or diagonally? We have given you a list to tick off, but one Pokémon is missing, found in the centre of the Poké Ball. Good luck!

```
          W E A V I L E N R
          B L S T W O B B S C R
          W I G G L Y T U F F W G C
      C H A R I Z A R D B E N L T C S B
      H W W P L N P I K R X R O B E R S
      A E O K E T S K O G O U R G E I S T M
      S S S B X B S N L A E Q V D L O L U C E B
      Q H P B I L N E C O Y C X Z D P L K T G B
  A Z S I U D Y I A K N B V L S P I I W C A W L
  P L H N F S C C S     C T K G S F C W C
  E T E U F F W D E     E L A R O V H A V
  B S L B E N L E L     P A C E P N A T V
  L N G R T R O D H     T P H N I R R N X
  S K O R U P I E A     I K U I W X I Y H
  P A N C H A M N P P Y V A L L L C N P B Z Y R
  O X Z G G Y N M L T S K O E S U J P L A C
  M O I Y G H E T E H A W L U C H A C W R T
      Y C D G O G W A O S E R E B E N P B D
      Y M H D A X W X N W P S F L W C V F U
          I Y H R U O E W T C J U P O K
          D G E L D W D E M H O C N S U
          H N P E G W C U V A B
          T A D E S A U S S
```

- ☐ CHARIZARD
- ☐ CHESPIN
- ☐ DEDENNE
- ☐ DRUDDIGON
- ☐ GOURGEIST
- ☐ GRENINJA
- ☐ HAWLUCHA
- ☐ HONEDGE
- ☐ INKAY
- ☐ MEGACHARIZARD
- ☐ MEOWTH
- ☐ PANCHAM
- ☐ POOCHYENA
- ☐ SCEPTILE
- ☐ SHELGON
- ☐ SKORUPI
- ☐ SNEASEL
- ☐ WEAVILE
- ☐ WIGGLYTUFF
- ☐ WOBBUFFET
- ☐ ZYGARDE

SEARCH & FIND

Pokémon can be sneaky creatures, and sometimes trying to catch them is harder than you think. It requires patience, practice and perseverance!!

Why not practice with your friends with this Search and Find game!

STEP 1

Simply cut out these characters using scissors (don't forget to ask a grown up for help, as scissors are sharp!).

STEP 2

Hide them around the house, or even in the garden.

STEP 3

See how long it takes your friends to find them, whoever finds all of their Pokémon in the fastest time, is the winner!

CHARMANDER

SQUIRTLE

PIKACHU

PANCHAM

DRUDDIGON

HAWLUCHA

CHARIZARD

MEOWTH

A to Z of POKÉMON

Follow our friends' adventures into the unchartered areas of the Pokémon World, the Kalos region and beyond. Our heroes never know what's around the next corner!!

This complete "A to Z" lists everyone of the wonderful types and species of Pokémon our heroes might stumble across on their adventures. Make sure you keep an eye out, and see if you can find some of the Kalos Region's Legendary Pokémon!!

With so many new adventures, and mysteries to be uncovered – it is sometimes hard to keep track of all of the different types of Pokémon they come across on their travels. Especially with the powerful and hard to find Mythical and Legendary Pokémon.

A to Z of POKÉMON

ABOMASNOW
TYPE: Grass - Ice
HEIGHT: 2.2m
WEIGHT: 135.5kg

Snow-covered mountains are Abomasnow's preferred habitat. It creates blizzards to hide itself and keep others away.

ABRA
TYPE: Psychic
HEIGHT: 0.9m
WEIGHT: 19.5kg

Even when it's asleep–which is most of the time–Abra can sense an attack coming and teleport away.

ABSOL
TYPE: Dark
HEIGHT: 1.2m
WEIGHT: 47.0kg

Absol doesn't often appear to people, but when it does, they should pay attention. It leaves its mountain home to warn others of an approaching disaster.

ACCELGOR
TYPE: Bug
HEIGHT: 0.8m
WEIGHT: 25.3kg

After coming out of its shell, Accelgor is light and quick, moving with the speed of a ninja. It wraps its body up to keep from drying out.

AEGISLASH
TYPE: Steel - Ghost
HEIGHT: 1.7m
WEIGHT: 53.0kg

Aegislash has long been seen as a symbol of royalty. In olden days, these Pokémon often accompanied the king.

AERODACTYL
TYPE: Rock - Flying
HEIGHT: 1.8m
WEIGHT: 59.0kg

This Pokémon was restored from a piece of fossilized amber. It's said that Aerodactyl ruled the skies in its ancient world.

AGGRON
TYPE: Steel - Rock
HEIGHT: 2.1m
WEIGHT: 360.0kg

Aggron is extremely protective of the mountain it claims as its territory. After a natural disaster, it will work tirelessly to restore its mountain, rebuilding the topsoil and planting trees.

AIPOM
TYPE: Normal
HEIGHT: 0.8m
WEIGHT: 11.5kg

Aipom uses the appendage at the end of its tail just like a hand. Its actual hands have lost their dexterity because it relies so much on its tail.

ALAKAZAM
TYPE: Psychic
HEIGHT: 1.5m
WEIGHT: 48.0kg

Because its brain never stops growing, Alakazam must use telekinesis to hold up its heavy head. On the plus side, its memory and intellect are amazing.

ALOMOMOLA
TYPE: Water
HEIGHT: 1.2m
WEIGHT: 31.6kg

When Alomomola finds injured Pokémon in the open sea where it lives, it gently wraps its healing fins around them and guides them to shore.

MYTHICAL

ARCEUS
TYPE: Normal
HEIGHT: 3.2m
WEIGHT: 320.0kg

In the mythology of the Sinnoh region, Arceus emerged from its Egg into complete nothingness, and then shaped the world and everything in it.

ALTARIA
TYPE: Dragon - Flying
HEIGHT: 1.1m
WEIGHT: 20.6kg

When Altaria sings through the sky in its beautiful soprano voice, anyone listening falls into a happy daydream. Its soft, cottony wings are perfect for catching updrafts.

AMAURA
TYPE: Rock - Ice
HEIGHT: 1.3m
WEIGHT: 25.2kg

In the ancient world, Amaura's cold habitat kept predators at bay. It was restored from a frozen fragment.

AMBIPOM
TYPE: Normal
HEIGHT: 1.2m
WEIGHT: 20.3kg

Because Ambipom's two tails are so dexterous, it rarely uses its arms after evolving. Groups of Ambipom will sometimes link tails as a sign of friendship.

AMOONGUSS
TYPE: Grass - Poison
HEIGHT: 0.6m
WEIGHT: 10.5kg

In a swaying dance, Amoonguss waves its arm caps, which look like Poké Balls, in an attempt to lure the unwary. It doesn't often work.

AMPHAROS
TYPE: Electric
HEIGHT: 1.4m
WEIGHT: 61.5kg

Ampharos shines so brightly that its light can be seen over long distances. Long ago, people used this light to send signals from far away.

ANORITH
TYPE: Rock - Bug
HEIGHT: 0.7m
WEIGHT: 12.5kg

The eight wings along Anorith's body wave in sequence to propel it through the warm seas where it lives. It was restored from a fossil.

LEGENDARY

ARTICUNO

TYPE: Ice - Flying
HEIGHT: 1.7m
WEIGHT: 55.4kg

When Articuno flaps its wings, the air turns chilly. This Legendary Pokémon often brings snowfall in its wake.

ARBOK

TYPE: Poison
HEIGHT: 3.5m
WEIGHT: 65.0kg

A powerful constrictor, Arbok can crush a steel barrel in its mighty coils. Getting out of its grip is no small feat.

ARCANINE

TYPE: Fire
HEIGHT: 1.9m
WEIGHT: 155.0kg

Arcanine's internal flame is the fuel for its amazing speed and endurance. If it runs for a whole day, it can cover more than 6,000 miles.

ARCHEN

TYPE: Rock - Flying
HEIGHT: 0.5m
WEIGHT: 9.5kg

It is believed that modern-day flying Pokémon descended from the ancient Archen, even though its wings aren't strong enough for flight. It was restored from a fossil.

ARCHEOPS

TYPE: Rock - Flying
HEIGHT: 1.4m
WEIGHT: 32.0kg

After evolving, Archeops can fly, though they aren't very good at it. They need a running start to get airborne and can generally get around more reliably by running.

ARIADOS

TYPE: Bug - Poison
HEIGHT: 1.12m
WEIGHT: 33.5kg

The web Ariados spins is made of thin silk, strong enough to bind and hold an enemy. The tiny hooks on its feet make it an excellent climber.

ARMALDO

TYPE: Rock - Bug
HEIGHT: 1.5m
WEIGHT: 68.2kg

With its huge claws and armored body, Armaldo is well equipped for battle. It has adapted to walk on its hind legs so it can live on land.

AROMATISSE

TYPE: Fairy
HEIGHT: 0.8m
WEIGHT: 15.5kg

Aromatisse uses its powerful scent as a weapon in battle. It can overpower an opponent with a strategic stench.

ARON

TYPE: Steel - Rock
HEIGHT: 0.4m
WEIGHT: 60.0kg

Aron chews up metal objects, from iron ore to steel bridges, and uses the metal to build up its body. It can destroy a heavy truck with a full-speed charge.

AUDINO

TYPE: Normal
HEIGHT: 1.1m
WEIGHT: 31.0kg

With the sensitive feelers on their ears, Audino can listen to people's heartbeats to pick up on their current state. Egg-hatching can be predicted as well.

AURORUS

TYPE: Rock - Ice
HEIGHT: 2.7m
WEIGHT: 225.5kg

With the icy crystals that line its sides, Aurorus can freeze the surrounding air and trap its foes in ice.

AVALUGG

TYPE: Ice
HEIGHT: 2.0m
WEIGHT: 505.0kg

Avalugg's broad, flat back is a common resting place for groups of Bergmite. Its big, bulky body can crush obstacles in its path.

AXEW

TYPE: Dragon
HEIGHT: 0.6m
WEIGHT: 18.0kg

If one of Axew's tusks breaks off, it quickly regrows, even stronger and sharper than before. It uses its tusks to crush berries and mark territory.

LEGENDARY

AZELF

TYPE: Psychic
HEIGHT: 0.3m
WEIGHT: 0.3kg

According to legend, Azelf brought a lasting balance to the world. It is known as "The Being of Willpower."

AZUMARILL

TYPE: Water - Fairy
HEIGHT: 0.8m
WEIGHT: 28.5kg

When Azumarill spots a Pokémon struggling in the water, it creates a balloon of air so the other Pokémon can breathe. It has excellent hearing.

AZURILL

TYPE: Normal - Fairy
HEIGHT: 0.2m
WEIGHT: 2.0kg

Azurill can fling itself more than 10 yards by spinning the large ball at the end of its tail and then throwing it. It can also use the tail to bounce around.

BAGON

TYPE: Dragon
HEIGHT: 0.6m
WEIGHT: 41.2kg

Chasing its dream of flight, Bagon practices by jumping from high places. To protect it during these leaps, its head has become hard enough to smash boulders.

BALTOY
TYPE: Ground - Psychic
HEIGHT: 0.5m
WEIGHT: 21.5kg

Baltoy can spin on its single foot to keep itself upright when moving or sleeping. Apparently, these Pokémon lived among people in ancient times.

BANETTE
TYPE: Ghost
HEIGHT: 1.1m
WEIGHT: 12.5kg

Banette keeps its mouth zipped tightly shut so its energy doesn't escape. It sticks itself with pins to curse others.

BARBARACLE
TYPE: Rock - Water
HEIGHT: 1.3m
WEIGHT: 96.0kg

When seven Binacle come together to fight as one, a Barbaracle is formed. The head gives the orders, but the limbs don't always listen.

BARBOACH
TYPE: Water - Ground
HEIGHT: 0.4m
WEIGHT: 1.9kg

Barboach buries itself in the mud, leaving its whiskers exposed to sense when something is moving nearby. The slimy coating on its body makes it very hard to grab.

BASCULIN
TYPE: Water
HEIGHT: 1.0m
WEIGHT: 18.0kg

An ongoing feud exists between Basculin with blue stripes and Basculin with red stripes. Because they're constantly fighting, they are rarely found in the same place.

BASTIODON
TYPE: Rock - Steel
HEIGHT: 1.3m
WEIGHT: 149.5kg

When several Bastiodon stand shoulder to shoulder, no attack can penetrate the shield wall formed by their rocky faces. Despite their imposing appearance, they are quite gentle.

BAYLEEF
TYPE: Grass
HEIGHT: 1.2m
WEIGHT: 15.8kg

The tree shoots that form a wreath around Bayleef's neck give off an invigorating fragrance. A tube-shaped leaf protects each shoot.

BEARTIC
TYPE: Ice
HEIGHT: 2.6m
WEIGHT: 260.0kg

Beartic live in the far north, where the seas are very cold. Their fangs and claws are made of ice formed by their own freezing breath.

BEAUTIFLY
TYPE: Bug - Flying
HEIGHT: 1.0m
WEIGHT: 28.4kg

To attract a Beautifly, plant flowers near your windows. This Pokémon uncoils its long mouth to gather pollen from flowers.

BEEDRILL
TYPE: Bug - Poison
HEIGHT: 1.0m
WEIGHT: 29.5kg

Stay far away from a Beedrill nest. These territorial Pokémon will swarm any intruder in a furious attack.

BEHEEYEM
TYPE: Psychic
HEIGHT: 1.0m
WEIGHT: 34.5kg

Beheeyem flashes its fingers in three different colors to communicate, but the patterns aren't yet understood. With its psychic power, it can take control of an opponent's mind.

BELDUM
TYPE: Steel - Psychic
HEIGHT: 0.6m
WEIGHT: 95.2kg

The magnetic force that runs through Beldum's body keeps it hovering in midair. It can send magnetic pulses to communicate with others.

BELLOSSOM
TYPE: Grass
HEIGHT: 0.4m
WEIGHT: 5.8kg

In strong sunlight, this Pokémon's leaves spin in a joyful dance. Bellossom that evolve from a particularly stinky Gloom will grow the most beautiful flowers.

BELLSPROUT
TYPE: Grass - Poison
HEIGHT: 0.7m
WEIGHT: 4.0kg

Bellsprout's long, thin body can bend in any direction, so it's good at dodging attacks. The liquid it spits is highly corrosive.

BERGMITE
TYPE: Ice
HEIGHT: 1.0m
WEIGHT: 99.5kg

When cracks form in Bergmite's icy body, it uses freezing air to patch itself up with new ice. It lives high in the mountains.

BIBAREL
TYPE: Normal - Water
HEIGHT: 1.0m
WEIGHT: 31.5kg

With their large, sharp teeth, Bibarel busily cut up trees to build nests. Sometimes these nests block small streams and divert the flow of the water.

BIDOOF
TYPE: Normal
HEIGHT: 0.5m
WEIGHT: 20.0kg

Bidoof live beside the water, where they gnaw on rock or wood to keep their front teeth worn down. They have a steady nature and are not easily upset.

BINACLE
TYPE: Rock - Water
HEIGHT: 0.5m
WEIGHT: 31.0kg

Binacle live in pairs, two on the same rock. They comb the beach for seaweed to eat.

BISHARP

TYPE:	Dark - Steel
HEIGHT:	1.6m
WEIGHT:	70.0kg

When Pawniard hunt in a pack, Bisharp leads them and gives the orders. It's often the one that deals the final blow.

BLASTOISE

TYPE:	Water
HEIGHT:	1.6m
WEIGHT:	85.5kg

From the spouts on its shell, Blastoise can fire water bullets with amazing accuracy. It can hit a target more than 160 feet away!

BLAZIKEN

TYPE:	Fire - Fighting
HEIGHT:	1.9m
WEIGHT:	52.0kg

With continued strengthening of its legs, Blaziken can leap over a 30-story building. The flames that flare from its wrists burn hotter against a worthy foe.

BLISSEY

TYPE:	Normal
HEIGHT:	1.5m
WEIGHT:	46.8kg

Blissey is extremely sensitive to people's emotions. If it senses sorrow, it leaps into action, rushing to the sad person's side with the gift of a special egg.

BLITZLE

TYPE:	Electric
HEIGHT:	0.8m
WEIGHT:	29.8kg

Blitzle's mane attracts lightning and stores the electricity. It can discharge this electricity in controlled flashes to communicate with others.

BOLDORE

TYPE:	Rock
HEIGHT:	0.9m
WEIGHT:	102.0kg

The energy within Boldore's body overflows, leaks out, and forms into orange crystals. Though its head always points in the same direction, it can quickly move sideways and backward.

BONSLY

TYPE:	Rock
HEIGHT:	0.5m
WEIGHT:	15.0kg

Bonsly prefers to live in dry places. When its body is storing excess moisture, it releases water from its eyes, making it look like it's crying.

BOUFFALANT

TYPE:	Normal
HEIGHT:	1.6m
WEIGHT:	94.6kg

Though Bouffalant can knock a train off the rails with the force of its headbutt, it doesn't worry about hurting itself, because its fluffy fur absorbs the impact.

BRAIXEN

TYPE:	Fire
HEIGHT:	1.0m
WEIGHT:	14.5kg

When Braixen pulls the twig out of its tail, the friction from its fur sets the wood on fire. It can use this flaming twig as a tool or a weapon.

BRAVIARY

TYPE:	Normal - Flying
HEIGHT:	1.5m
WEIGHT:	41.0kg

To protect its friends, Braviary will keep battling even when it's hurt. Its wings and talons are so strong that it can carry a car through the air.

BRELOOM

TYPE:	Grass - Fighting
HEIGHT:	1.2m
WEIGHT:	39.2kg

If a seed falls from Breloom's tail, you really shouldn't eat it. The seeds are toxic and taste terrible. Its arms stretch to throw impressive punches.

BRONZONG

TYPE:	Steel - Psychic
HEIGHT:	1.3m
WEIGHT:	187.0kg

In ancient times, people thought Bronzong was responsible for making the rain fall, so they often asked it for help to make their crops flourish.

BRONZOR

TYPE:	Steel - Psychic
HEIGHT:	0.5m
WEIGHT:	60.5kg

In ancient times, people thought a mystical power was contained within Bronzor's back pattern. Artifacts matching its shape have been discovered in tombs from that era.

BUDEW

TYPE:	Grass - Poison
HEIGHT:	0.2m
WEIGHT:	1.2kg

When the weather turns cold, Budew's bud is tightly closed. In the springtime, it opens up again and gives off its pollen.

BUIZEL

TYPE:	Water
HEIGHT:	0.7m
WEIGHT:	29.5kg

Buizel rapidly spins its two tails to propel itself through the water. The flotation sac around its neck keeps its head up without effort, and it can deflate the sac to dive.

BULBASAUR

TYPE:	Grass - Poison
HEIGHT:	0.7m
WEIGHT:	6.9kg

Bulbasaur likes to take a nap in the sunshine. While it sleeps, the seed on its back catches the rays and uses the energy to grow.

BUNEARY

TYPE: Normal
HEIGHT: 0.4m
WEIGHT: 5.5kg

Buneary keeps its ears rolled up except when attacking or scouting for danger. It can extend its ears with enough force to pulverize a boulder.

BUNNELBY

TYPE: Normal
HEIGHT: 0.4m
WEIGHT: 5.0kg

Bunnelby can use its ears like shovels to dig holes in the ground. Eventually, its ears become strong enough to cut through thick tree roots while it digs.

BURMY

TYPE: Bug
HEIGHT: 0.2m
WEIGHT: 3.4kg

Burmy creates a cloak for itself out of whatever materials it can find. The cloak protects it from chilly temperatures and shields it in battle.

BUTTERFREE

TYPE: Bug - Flying
HEIGHT: 1.1m
WEIGHT: 32.0kg

Butterfree is excellent at seeking out flowers with the most delicious nectar. It sometimes flies more than six miles to locate its favorite food.

CACNEA

TYPE: Grass
HEIGHT: 0.4m
WEIGHT: 51.3kg

Cacnea produce the most beautiful and fragrant flowers when they live in particularly harsh and dry environments. They can shoot their thorns to attack.

CACTURNE

TYPE: Grass - Dark
HEIGHT: 1.3m
WEIGHT: 77.4kg

Cacturne stand very still during the day so as not to waste energy or moisture in the heat of the desert sun. After dark, they hunt in packs, often attacking travelers who weren't prepared for the environment.

CAMERUPT

TYPE: Fire - Ground
HEIGHT: 1.9m
WEIGHT: 220.0kg

When Camerupt gets angry, the volcanic humps on its back tend to erupt. The magma that sprays out is superheated and very dangerous.

CARBINK

TYPE: Rock - Fairy
HEIGHT: 0.3m
WEIGHT: 5.7kg

While excavating caves, miners and archeologists sometimes stumble upon Carbink sleeping deep underground. The stone on top of its head can fire beams of energy.

CARNIVINE

TYPE: Grass
HEIGHT: 1.4m
WEIGHT: 27.0kg

Carnivine wraps itself around trees in swampy areas. It gives off a sweet aroma that lures others close, then attacks.

CARRACOSTA

TYPE: Water - Rock
HEIGHT: 1.2m
WEIGHT: 81.0kg

With its powerful jaws and massive front flippers, Carracosta is a formidable fighter. It can break through the hull of a tanker ship with a single slap.

CARVANHA

TYPE: Water - Dark
HEIGHT: 0.8m
WEIGHT: 20.8kg

Carvanha descend in a swarm to attack anything that enters their territory. When they work together, their strong jaws and sharp teeth can rip a hole in a boat's hull.

CASCOON

TYPE: Bug
HEIGHT: 0.7m
WEIGHT: 11.5kg

When Cascoon is ready to evolve, it wraps itself up in silk, which hardens around its body. If something attacks its cocoon, it takes the hit without moving so as not to use up energy... but it also remembers the attacker.

CASTFORM

TYPE: Normal
HEIGHT: 0.3m
WEIGHT: 0.8kg

Changes in the weather alter Castform's appearance and its mood. It draws on the power of nature to transform and protect itself from the elements.

CATERPIE

TYPE: Bug
HEIGHT: 0.2m
WEIGHT: 2.9kg

A ravenous Caterpie can quickly gobble up leaves that are bigger than itself. Its antenna can produce a terrible smell.

CHANDELURE

TYPE: Ghost - Fire
HEIGHT: 1.0m
WEIGHT: 34.3kg

Chandelure's spooky flames can burn the spirit right out of someone. If that happens, the spirit becomes trapped in this world, endlessly wandering.

MYTHICAL

CELEBI

TYPE: Psychic - Grass
HEIGHT: 0.6m
WEIGHT: 5.0kg

Celebi traveled back in time to come to this world. According to myth, its presence is a sign of a bright future.

CHANSEY

TYPE: Normal
HEIGHT: 1.1m
WEIGHT: 34.6kg

The eggs Chansey produces every day are full of nutrition and flavor. Even people suffering a loss of appetite eat them up with delight.

CHARMANDER

TYPE: Fire
HEIGHT: 0.6m
WEIGHT: 8.5kg

The flame on Charmander's tail tip indicates how the Pokémon is feeling. It flares up in a fury when Charmander is angry!

CHARIZARD

TYPE: Fire - Flying	Charizard seeks out stronger foes and only breathes fire
HEIGHT: 1.7m	during battles with worthy opponents. The fiery breath is
WEIGHT: 90.5kg	so hot that it can turn any material to slag.

CHARMELEON

TYPE: Fire
HEIGHT: 1.1m
WEIGHT: 19.0kg

When Charmeleon takes on a powerful opponent in battle, its tail flame glows white-hot. Its claws are very sharp.

CHATOT

TYPE: Normal - Flying
HEIGHT: 0.5m
WEIGHT: 1.9kg

Chatot can mimic other Pokémon's cries and even human speech. A group of them will often pick up the same phrase and keep repeating it among themselves.

CHERRIM

TYPE: Grass
HEIGHT: 0.5m
WEIGHT: 9.3kg

Cherrim keeps its petals folded around itself except in bright sunshine. When the weather is nice, its bloom opens wide to absorb as much sunlight as it can.

CHERUBI

TYPE: Grass
HEIGHT: 0.4m
WEIGHT: 3.3kg

Cherubi stores nutrients in the small red ball attached to its head. When it's ready to evolve, it uses up all the nutrients at once, making the small ball wither.

CHESNAUGHT

TYPE: Grass - Fighting
HEIGHT: 1.6m
WEIGHT: 90.0kg

When its friends are in trouble, Chesnaught uses its own body as a shield. Its shell is tough enough to protect it from a powerful explosion.

CHESPIN

TYPE: Grass
HEIGHT: 0.4m
WEIGHT: 9.0kg

When Chespin flexes its soft quills, they become tough spikes with sharp, piercing points. It relies on its nutlike shell for protection in battle.

CHIKORITA

TYPE: Grass
HEIGHT: 0.9m
WEIGHT: 6.4kg

Chikorita brandishes its leaf in battle to fend off a foe. When it does this, the leaf gives off a lovely aroma that calms everyone down.

CHIMCHAR

TYPE: Fire
HEIGHT: 0.5m
WEIGHT: 6.2kg

Chimchar's rear is always on fire, even when it stands in the rain. If it's not feeling well, the flame flickers weakly.

CHIMECHO

TYPE: Psychic
HEIGHT: 0.6m
WEIGHT: 1.0kg

The sucker on the top of Chimecho's head can attach to a tree branch or building. Its hollow body amplifies its chiming cries.

CHINCHOU

TYPE: Water - Electric
HEIGHT: 0.5m
WEIGHT: 12.0kg

With its two antennae, Chinchou can release an electric charge for use as a weapon, or flash lights to communicate. It sometimes gets a tingly feeling if it generates too much electricity.

CHINGLING

TYPE: Psychic
HEIGHT: 0.2m
WEIGHT: 0.6kg

When Chingling hops about, a small orb bounces around inside its mouth, producing a noise like the sound of bells. It uses high-pitched sounds to attack its opponents' hearing.

CINCCINO

TYPE: Normal
HEIGHT: 0.5m
WEIGHT: 7.5kg

A special oil coats Cinccino's soft white fur. This oil repels dust and dirt, deflects enemy attacks, and keeps static electricity at bay.

CLAMPERL

TYPE: Water
HEIGHT: 0.4m
WEIGHT: 52.5kg

Even as Clamperl's soft body grows inside its hard shell, the shell stays the same size until it evolves. In addition to protecting itself, it uses the shell to catch food, or to grab onto an opponent in battle.

CLAUNCHER

TYPE: Water
HEIGHT: 0.5m
WEIGHT: 8.3kg

Clauncher shoots water from its claws with a force that can pulverize rock. Its range is great enough to knock flying Pokémon out of the air.

CLAWITZER
TYPE: Water
HEIGHT: 1.3m
WEIGHT: 35.3kg

Clawitzer's giant claw can expel massive jets of water at high speed. It fires the water forward to attack, or backward to propel itself through the sea.

CLAYDOL
TYPE: Ground - Psychic
HEIGHT: 1.5m
WEIGHT: 108.0kg

Claydol is thought to have originated from an ancient clay statue. It levitates to move and can shoot energy beams from its hands.

CLEFABLE
TYPE: Fairy
HEIGHT: 1.3m
WEIGHT: 40.0kg

Clefable moves with such lightness that it can skip across the water—perfect for a moonlight stroll on the surface of a lake.

CLEFAIRY
TYPE: Fairy
HEIGHT: 0.6m
WEIGHT: 7.5kg

Groups of Clefairy gather to play under the full moon. When the sun rises, they retreat to their mountain home and snuggle together to sleep.

CLEFFA
TYPE: Fairy
HEIGHT: 0.3m
WEIGHT: 3.0kg

During a meteor shower, groups of Cleffa gather to dance in a circle. Their dance lasts until dawn and makes them very thirsty, so they sip dewdrops to rehydrate.

CLOYSTER
TYPE: Water - Ice
HEIGHT: 1.5m
WEIGHT: 132.5kg

By sucking in water and then shooting it out, Cloyster can propel itself through the sea. It also uses this method to fire its shell spikes in battle.

LEGENDARY

COBALION
TYPE: Steel - Fighting
HEIGHT: 2.1m
WEIGHT: 250.0kg

Like its body, Cobalion's heart is tough as steel. Legends say that in the past, it protected Pokémon from harmful people.

COFAGRIGUS
TYPE: Ghost
HEIGHT: 1.7m
WEIGHT: 76.5kg

Cofagrigus resembles a coffin covered in solid gold. Stories say that when would-be thieves approach, it opens its lid and traps them inside.

COMBEE
TYPE: Bug - Flying
HEIGHT: 0.3m
WEIGHT: 5.5kg

Combee are always in search of honey, which they bring to their Vespiquen leader. They cluster together to sleep in a formation that resembles a hive.

COMBUSKEN
TYPE: Fire - Fighting
HEIGHT: 0.9m
WEIGHT: 19.5kg

Combusken runs through meadows and up mountains to strengthen its legs. It can deliver kicks at high speed and with crushing power.

CONKELDURR
TYPE: Fighting
HEIGHT: 1.4m
WEIGHT: 87.0kg

Conkeldurr spin their concrete pillars to attack. It's said that long ago, people first learned about concrete from these Pokémon.

CORPHISH
TYPE: Water
HEIGHT: 0.6m
WEIGHT: 11.5kg

Corphish aren't picky about what they eat or where they live. Because of this, their numbers have increased substantially.

CORSOLA
TYPE: Water - Rock
HEIGHT: 0.6m
WEIGHT: 5.0kg

Corsola prefer warm water and migrate south when it gets cold. When the sun hits their branches just right, they sparkle in many colors.

COTTONEE
TYPE: Grass - Fairy
HEIGHT: 0.3m
WEIGHT: 0.6kg

When threatened, it releases cotton from its body to act as a decoy while it escapes. When several Cottonee stick together, they resemble a cloud drifting through the sky.

CRADILY
TYPE: Rock - Grass
HEIGHT: 1.5m
WEIGHT: 60.4kg

After evolving, Cradily leaves its rock and wanders freely to find food along the bottom of the sea. It can also anchor its body to withstand rough seas.

CRANIDOS
TYPE: Rock
HEIGHT: 0.9m
WEIGHT: 31.5kg

Cranidos lived in the ancient jungle and cleared its path by headbutting trees to make them fall down. It was restored from a fossil.

LEGENDARY

CRESSELIA
TYPE: Psychic
HEIGHT: 1.5m
WEIGHT: 85.6kg

The glimmering particles that trail from Cresselia's wings resemble a veil. This Legendary Pokémon, which brings happy dreams, is said to be a symbol of the crescent moon.

CRAWDAUNT
TYPE: Water - Dark
HEIGHT: 1.1m
WEIGHT: 32.8kg

Crawdaunt doesn't tolerate company, and if another Pokémon enters its territory, it's in for a battle. The only time Crawdaunt isn't itching for a fight is just after it sheds its shell, when its soft body is vulnerable.

CROAGUNK
TYPE: Poison - Fighting
HEIGHT: 0.7m
WEIGHT: 23.0kg

Croagunk produces its distinctive croaking sound by inflating the poison sacs in its cheeks. The sound often startles an opponent so it can get in a poisonous jab.

CROBAT
TYPE: Poison - Flying
HEIGHT: 1.8m
WEIGHT: 75.0kg

Crobat's four wings cut through the air with barely a sound. If it's been flying a long way, it starts alternating wings, flapping with one pair and letting the other pair rest.

CROCONAW
TYPE: Water
HEIGHT: 1.1m
WEIGHT: 25.0kg

Each of Croconaw's fangs ends in a barb that resembles a fishhook. When it grips a foe in its fearsome jaws, escape is nearly impossible.

CRUSTLE
TYPE: Bug - Rock
HEIGHT: 1.4m
WEIGHT: 200.0kg

Because Crustle carries a heavy slab of rock everywhere it goes, its legs are extremely strong. Battles between them are determined by whose rock breaks first.

CRYOGONAL
TYPE: Ice
HEIGHT: 1.1m
WEIGHT: 148.0kg

Cryogonal's crystalline structure is made of ice formed in snow clouds. With its long chains of ice crystals, it unleashes a freezing attack.

CUBCHOO
TYPE: Ice
HEIGHT: 0.5m
WEIGHT: 8.5kg

Even a healthy Cubchoo always has a runny nose. Its sniffles power its freezing attacks.

CUBONE
TYPE: Ground
HEIGHT: 0.4m
WEIGHT: 6.5kg

When Cubone looks at the full moon, it often sees an image of its lost mother. Its tears leave stains on the skull it wears.

CYNDAQUIL
TYPE: Fire
HEIGHT: 0.5m
WEIGHT: 7.9kg

The protective flames on Cyndaquil's back are an indicator of its mood. A sputtering fire means it's tired, while anger makes the flames burn high and hot.

DARMANITAN
TYPE: Fire
HEIGHT: 1.3m
WEIGHT: 92.9kg

Fueled by its internal fire, Darmanitan can throw a punch hard enough to destroy a dump truck. To recover from a serious battle, it turns to stone so it can meditate undisturbed.

DARKRAI
MYTHICAL
TYPE: Dark
HEIGHT: 1.5m
WEIGHT: 50.5kg

Darkrai defends its territory by sending intruders into a deep sleep, where they are tormented by terrible nightmares.

DARUMAKA
TYPE: Fire
HEIGHT: 0.6m
WEIGHT: 37.5kg

Darumaka tucks its hands and feet into its body to sleep, but its internal fire still burns at searing temperatures. Long ago, people used its intense body heat to warm themselves.

DEDENNE
TYPE: Electric - Fairy
HEIGHT: 0.2m
WEIGHT: 2.2kg

Dedenne uses its whiskers like antennas to communicate over long distances using electrical waves. It can soak up electricity through its tail.

DEERLING
TYPE: Normal - Grass
HEIGHT: 0.6m
WEIGHT: 19.5kg

Deerling's fur changes with the seasons. Shifts in temperature and humidity affect the color and even the scent of its fur.

DEINO
TYPE: Dark - Dragon
HEIGHT: 0.8m
WEIGHT: 17.3kg

Deino can't see, so they explore their surroundings by biting and crashing into things. Because of this, they are often covered in cuts and scratches.

DELCATTY
TYPE: Normal
HEIGHT: 1.1m
WEIGHT: 32.6kg

Delcatty lives according to its own whims, eating and sleeping as the mood strikes it. If awakened by another Pokémon, it moves elsewhere to continue its nap.

DELIBIRD
TYPE: Ice - Flying
HEIGHT: 0.9m
WEIGHT: 16.0kg

With Delibird's help, a famous climber was able to summit the tallest mountain in the world! This Pokémon always stores extra food in its rolled-up tail and shares it with travelers.

DEOXYS
LEGENDARY
TYPE: Psychic
HEIGHT: 1.7m
WEIGHT: 60.8kg

From the crystal on its chest, Deoxys can shoot out laser beams. This highly intelligent Pokémon came into being when a virus mutated during a fall from space.

DELPHOX
TYPE: Fire - Psychic
HEIGHT: 1.5m
WEIGHT: 39.0kg

The mystical Delphox uses a flaming branch as a focus for its psychic visions. When it gazes into the fire, it can see the future.

DEWGONG
TYPE: Water - Ice
HEIGHT: 1.7m
WEIGHT: 120.0kg

Long ago, a sailor saw Dewgong taking a nap on the ice and thought it was a mermaid. It sleeps best in the bitter cold.

DEWOTT
TYPE: Water
HEIGHT: 0.8m
WEIGHT: 24.5kg

Dewott must undergo disciplined training to master the flowing techniques it uses when wielding its two scalchops in battle.

LEGENDARY

DIALGA
TYPE: Steel - Dragon
HEIGHT: 5.4m
WEIGHT: 683.0kg

It is said Dialga can control time with its mighty roar. In ancient times, it was revered as a legend.

MYTHICAL

DIANCIE
TYPE: Rock - Fairy
HEIGHT: 0.7m
WEIGHT: 8.8kg

According to myth, when Carbink suddenly transforms into Diancie, its dazzling appearance is the most beautiful sight in existence. It has the power to compress carbon from the atmosphere, forming diamonds between its hands.

DIGGERSBY
TYPE: Normal - Ground
HEIGHT: 1.0m
WEIGHT: 42.4kg

Diggersby can use their ears like excavators to move heavy boulders. Construction workers like having them around.

DIGLETT
TYPE: Ground
HEIGHT: 0.2m
WEIGHT: 0.8kg

Farmers love having Diglett around. As these Pokémon burrow through the ground, they leave the soil in perfect condition for planting.

DITTO
TYPE: Normal
HEIGHT: 0.3m
WEIGHT: 4.0kg

Ditto can alter the structure of its cells to change its shape. This works best if it has an example to copy–if it tries to copy another shape from memory, it sometimes gets things wrong.

DODRIO
TYPE: Normal - Flying
HEIGHT: 1.8m
WEIGHT: 85.2kg

Dodrio has three heads, three hearts, and three sets of lungs. It can keep watch in all directions and run a long way without getting tired.

DODUO
TYPE: Normal - Flying
HEIGHT: 1.4m
WEIGHT: 39.2kg

While one of Doduo's heads sleeps, the other stays alert to watch for danger. Its brains are identical.

DONPHAN
TYPE: Ground
HEIGHT: 1.1m
WEIGHT: 120.0kg

Donphan curls up in a ball to attack with a high-speed rolling tackle. Such an attack can knock down a house!

DOUBLADE
TYPE: Steel - Ghost
HEIGHT: 0.8m
WEIGHT: 4.5kg

The two swords that make up Doublade's body fight together in intricate slashing patterns that bewilder even accomplished swordsmen.

DRAGALGE
TYPE: Poison - Dragon
HEIGHT: 1.8m
WEIGHT: 81.5kg

Toxic and territorial, Dragalge defend their homes from anything that enters. Even large ships aren't safe from their poison.

DRAGONAIR
TYPE: Dragon
HEIGHT: 4.0m
WEIGHT: 16.5kg

Dragonair's internal energy can be discharged from special crystals on its body. Apparently, when this happens, it can change the local weather.

DRAGONITE
TYPE: Dragon - Flying
HEIGHT: 2.2m
WEIGHT: 210.0kg

Dragonite can fly around the whole world in less than a day. When it spies a ship in danger on the stormy ocean, it guides the crew safely to land.

DRAPION
TYPE: Poison - Dark
HEIGHT: 1.3m
WEIGHT: 61.5kg

Drapion's strong arms could tear a car into scrap metal. The claws on its arms and tail are extremely toxic.

DRATINI
TYPE: Dragon
HEIGHT: 1.8m
WEIGHT: 3.3kg

As Dratini grows, it is constantly in molt, shedding its skin to accommodate the life energy that builds up within it.

DRIFBLIM
TYPE: Ghost - Flying
HEIGHT: 1.2m
WEIGHT: 15.0kg

During the day, Drifblim tend to be sleepy. They take flight at dusk, but since they can't control their direction, they'll drift away wherever the wind blows them.

DRIFLOON
TYPE: Ghost - Flying
HEIGHT: 0.4m
WEIGHT: 1.2kg

Known as the "Signpost for Wandering Spirits," Drifloon itself was formed by spirits. It prefers humid weather and is happiest when it's floating through damp air.

DRILBUR
TYPE: Ground
HEIGHT: 0.3m
WEIGHT: 8.5kg

Drilbur bores through the ground by bringing its claws together to form a sharp point and rotating its entire body. In this way, it can travel underground as fast as 30 mph.

DROWZEE
TYPE: Psychic
HEIGHT: 1.0m
WEIGHT: 32.4kg

Ever wake up with an itchy nose? It might be because a Drowzee was lurking nearby, trying to draw out your dreams.

DRUDDIGON
TYPE: Dragon
HEIGHT: 1.6m
WEIGHT: 139.0kg

Druddigon can't move if it gets too cold, so it soaks up the sun with its wings. It can navigate tight caves at a brisk pace.

DUCKLETT
TYPE: Water - Flying
HEIGHT: 0.5m
WEIGHT: 5.5kg

Skilled swimmers, Ducklett dive underwater in search of delicious peat moss. When enemies approach, they kick up water with their wings to cover their retreat.

DUGTRIO
TYPE: Ground
HEIGHT: 0.7m
WEIGHT: 33.3kg

When it comes to digging, Dugtrio knows that three heads are better than one. The triplets think alike and work together.

DUNSPARCE
TYPE: Normal
HEIGHT: 1.5m
WEIGHT: 14.0kg

Dunsparce uses its tail like a drill to dig a burrow, scooting backward into the tunnel. Its underground nest is like a maze.

DUOSION
TYPE: Psychic
HEIGHT: 0.6m
WEIGHT: 8.0kg

Duosion's brain is divided into two, so sometimes it tries to do two different things at the same time. When the brains are thinking together, Duosion's psychic power is at its strongest.

DURANT
TYPE: Bug - Steel
HEIGHT: 0.3m
WEIGHT: 33.3kg

The heavily armored Durant work together to keep attackers away from their colony. Durant and Heatmor are natural enemies.

DUSCLOPS
TYPE: Ghost
HEIGHT: 1.6m
WEIGHT: 30.6kg

There is no escape for anything absorbed into the hollow body of Dusclops. When it waves its hands and focuses its single eye, it can entrance a foe to do its will.

DUSKNOIR
TYPE: Ghost
HEIGHT: 2.2m
WEIGHT: 106.6kg

Dusknoir senses signals from the spirit world with the antenna on its head. The signals tell it to guide lost spirits...and sometimes people.

DUSKULL
TYPE: Ghost
HEIGHT: 0.8m
WEIGHT: 15.0kg

Parents sometimes threaten misbehaving children with a visit from Duskull. It can pass through walls in pursuit of its target, but gives up the chase at sunrise.

DUSTOX
TYPE: Bug - Poison
HEIGHT: 1.2m
WEIGHT: 31.6kg

City lights attract Dustox in swarms. This is unfortunate, because their wings scatter poisonous dust and their feeding habits quickly strip trees bare.

DWEBBLE
TYPE: Bug - Rock
HEIGHT: 0.3m
WEIGHT: 14.5kg

Using a special liquid from its mouth, Dwebble hollows out a rock to use as its shell. It becomes very anxious without a proper rock.

EELEKTRIK
TYPE: Electric
HEIGHT: 1.2m
WEIGHT: 22.0kg

Eelektrik wraps its long body around its opponent and gives off a paralyzing electric shock from the round markings on its sides. Its appetite is quite large.

EELEKTROSS
TYPE: Electric
HEIGHT: 2.1m
WEIGHT: 80.5kg

With their gaping sucker mouths, electrically charged fangs, and long arms that allow them to crawl up on land, Eelektross are dangerous opponents.

EEVEE
TYPE: Normal
HEIGHT: 0.3m
WEIGHT: 6.5kg

The amazingly adaptive Eevee can evolve into many different Pokémon depending on its environment. Certain stones can trigger its Evolution.

EKANS
TYPE: Poison
HEIGHT: 2.0m
WEIGHT: 6.9kg

When Ekans rests, it coils its long body up into a spiral. In this position, it can quickly raise its head to challenge a foe.

ELECTABUZZ
TYPE: Electric
HEIGHT: 1.1m
WEIGHT: 30.0kg

During thunderstorms, Electabuzz climb to high places, hoping to be struck by lightning. Because they can absorb the bolts safely, they sometimes act as lightning rods.

ELECTIVIRE
TYPE: Electric
HEIGHT: 1.8m
WEIGHT: 138.6kg

Electricity crackles between Electivire's horns and the tips of its tails. When it forms a circuit with its tails, its opponent receives a powerful shock.

ELECTRIKE
TYPE: Electirc
HEIGHT: 0.6m
WEIGHT: 15.2kg

Electrike's long fur stores up static electricity when it runs at blinding speed. It can use this electricity to charge up its leg muscles and run even faster.

ELECTRODE
TYPE: Electric
HEIGHT: 1.2m
WEIGHT: 66.6kg

Electrode feeds by absorbing electricity, often from power plants or lightning storms. If it eats too much at once, it explodes.

ELEKID
TYPE: Electric
HEIGHT: 0.6m
WEIGHT: 23.5kg

Elekid tries to avoid touching metal, because doing so discharges the electricity it stores inside its body. If that happens, it spins its arms to charge up again.

ELGYEM
TYPE: Psychic
HEIGHT: 0.5m
WEIGHT: 9.0kg

It's said Elgyem were first discovered in the desert after a UFO crashed there 50 years ago. Their psychic power can compress an opponent's brain and cause terrible headaches.

EMBOAR
TYPE: Fire - Fighting
HEIGHT: 1.6m
WEIGHT: 150.0kg

With the fiery beard that covers its chin, Emboar can set its fists ablaze and throw flaming punches. Its battle moves are speedy and powerful.

EMOLGA
TYPE: Electric - Flying
HEIGHT: 0.4m
WEIGHT: 5.0kg

When Emolga stretches out its limbs, the membrane connecting them spreads like a cape and allows it to glide through the air. It makes its abode high in the trees.

EMPOLEON
TYPE: Water - Steel
HEIGHT: 1.7m
WEIGHT: 84.5kg

With the sharp edges of its wings, Empoleon can slash through drifting ice as it swims faster than a speedboat. The length of its trident-like horns indicates its power.

LEGENDARY

ESCAVALIER
TYPE: Bug - Steel
HEIGHT: 1.0m
WEIGHT: 33.0kg

The stolen Shelmet shell protects Escavalier's body like armor. It uses its double lances to attack.

ESPEON
TYPE: Psychic
HEIGHT: 0.9m
WEIGHT: 26.5kg

When Espeon finds its Trainer worthy, its loyalty knows no bounds. It apparently learned to predict danger so it could keep its Trainer safe.

ESPURR
TYPE: Psychic
HEIGHT: 0.3m
WEIGHT: 3.5kg

Espurr emits powerful psychic energy from organs in its ears. It has to fold its ears down to keep the power contained.

ENTEI
TYPE: Fire
HEIGHT: 2.1m
WEIGHT: 198.0kg

People say that Entei came into being when a volcano erupted. This Legendary Pokémon carries the heat of magma in its fiery heart.

EXCADRILL
TYPE: Ground - Steel
HEIGHT: 0.7m
WEIGHT: 40.4kg

Excadrill live several hundred feet underground, where they use their strong steel claws to dig out nests and tunnels. Sometimes that causes big trouble for subway systems.

EXEGGCUTE
TYPE: Grass - Psychic
HEIGHT: 0.4m
WEIGHT: 2.5kg

The six eggs that make up Exeggcute's body spin around a common center. When the eggs begin to crack, this Pokémon is ready to evolve.

EXEGGUTOR
TYPE: Grass - Psychic
HEIGHT: 2.0m
WEIGHT: 120.0kg

A tropical Pokémon, Exeggutor has three heads that keep growing when they get enough sun. Exeggcute are thought to form from the fallen heads of Exeggutor.

EXPLOUD
TYPE: Normal
HEIGHT: 1.5m
WEIGHT: 84.0kg

When Exploud takes a deep breath through the tubes that cover its body, watch out! It's about to unleash a thunderous bellow that will shake the ground around it.

FARFETCH'D
TYPE: Normal - Flyimg
HEIGHT: 0.8m
WEIGHT: 15.0kg

Farfetch'd always carries its trusty plant stalk. Sometimes, two of them will fight over a superior stalk.

FEAROW
TYPE: Normal - Flying
HEIGHT: 1.2m
WEIGHT: 38.0kg

Fearow's long, thin beak is the perfect tool for digging up food from the dirt or catching it in the water.

FEEBAS
TYPE: Water
HEIGHT: 0.6m
WEIGHT: 7.4kg

Feebas isn't much to look at, but its hardy nature and persistent survival instinct let it live in any aquatic environment.

FENNEKIN
TYPE: Fire
HEIGHT: 0.4m
WEIGHT: 9.4kg

Searing heat radiates from Fennekin's large ears to keep opponents at a distance. It often snacks on twigs to gain energy.

FERALIGATR
TYPE: Water
HEIGHT: 2.3m
WEIGHT: 88.8kg

Feraligatr uses its gaping maw as an intimidation tactic. Its powerful legs propel it into a high-speed charge.

FERROSEED
TYPE: Grass - Steel
HEIGHT: 0.6m
WEIGHT: 18.8kg

Ferroseed use their spikes to cling to cave ceilings and absorb iron. They can also shoot those spikes to cover their escape when enemies approach.

FERROTHORN
TYPE: Grass - Steel
HEIGHT: 1.0m
WEIGHT: 110.0kg

Ferrothorn swings its spiked feelers to attack. It likes to hang from the ceiling of a cave and shower spikes on anyone passing below.

FINNEON
TYPE: Water
HEIGHT: 0.4m
WEIGHT: 7kg

If Finneon soaks up enough sunlight during the day, the patterns on its body give off light when night falls on the sea where it lives.

FLAAFFY
TYPE: Electric
HEIGHT: 0.8m
WEIGHT: 13.3kg

Parts of Flaaffy's body are covered in wool that generates static electricity and builds up a charge. Its skin is resistant to electricity, so it doesn't shock itself by accident.

FLABÉBÉ
TYPE: Fairy
HEIGHT: 0.1m
WEIGHT: 0.1kg

Each Flabébé has a special connection with the flower it holds. They take care of their flowers and use them as an energy source.

FLAREON
TYPE: Fire
HEIGHT: 0.9m
WEIGHT: 25.0kg

Flareon's body can become very hot, so it fluffs out its soft fur to release excess heat into its surroundings. Even so, it can reach more than 1,600 degrees Fahrenheit.

FLETCHINDER
TYPE: Normal - Flying
HEIGHT: 0.7m
WEIGHT: 16.0kg

As the flame sac on Fletchinder's belly slowly heats up, it flies faster and faster. It produces embers from its beak.

FLETCHLING
TYPE: Normal - Flying
HEIGHT: 0.3m
WEIGHT: 1.7kg

Flocks of Fletchling sing to each other in beautiful voices to communicate. If an intruder threatens their territory, they will defend it fiercely.

FLOATZEL
TYPE: Water
HEIGHT: 1.1m
WEIGHT: 33.5kg

The flotation sac that surrounds its entire body makes Floatzel very good at rescuing people in the water. It can float them to safety like an inflatable raft.

FLOETTE
TYPE: Fairy
HEIGHT: 0.2m
WEIGHT: 0.9kg

Floette keeps watch over flower beds and will rescue a flower if it starts to droop. It dances to celebrate the spring bloom.

FLORGES
TYPE: Fairy
HEIGHT: 1.1m
WEIGHT: 10.0kg

Long ago, Florges were a welcome sight on castle grounds, where they would create elaborate flower gardens.

FLYGON
TYPE: Ground - Dragon
HEIGHT: 20.0m
WEIGHT: 89.0kg

When Flygon flaps its wings, it stirs up the sand to create a concealing sandstorm. The vibration of the wings also produces musical tones, making it sound like the Pokémon is singing through the sandstorm.

FOONGUS
TYPE: Grass - Poison
HEIGHT: 0.2m
WEIGHT: 1.0kg

Foongus uses its deceptive Poké Ball pattern to lure people or Pokémon close. Then, it attacks with poison spores.

FORRETRESS
TYPE: Bug - Steel
HEIGHT: 1.2m
WEIGHT: 125.8kg

Forretress is protected by a shell of solid steel. It opens the shell to catch food, but slams it shut again so quickly that no one can see inside.

FRAXURE
TYPE: Dagon
HEIGHT: 1.0m
WEIGHT: 36.0kg

Fraxure clash in intense battles over territory. After a battle is over, they always remember to sharpen their tusks on smooth stones so they'll be ready for the next battle.

FRILLISH
TYPE: Water - Ghost
HEIGHT: 1.2m
WEIGHT: 33.0kg

When battling underwater, Frillish uses poison to stun its opponent, then wraps the foe in its veil-like arms and drags it down into the depths.

FROAKIE
TYPE: Water
HEIGHT: 0.3m
WEIGHT: 7.0kg

The foamy bubbles that cover Froakie's body protect its sensitive skin from damage. It's always alert to any changes in its environment.

FROGADIER
TYPE: Water
HEIGHT: 0.6m
WEIGHT: 10.9kg

Swift and sure, Frogadier coats pebbles in a bubbly foam and then flings them with pinpoint accuracy. It has spectacular jumping and climbing skills.

FROSLASS
TYPE: Ice - Ghost
HEIGHT: 1.3m
WEIGHT: 26.6kg

With its icy breath, Froslass can freeze its opponents solid. Some believe the first Froslass was created when a woman became lost in the snowy mountains.

FURFROU
TYPE: Normal
HEIGHT: 1.2m
WEIGHT: 28.0kg

An experienced groomer can trim Furfrou's fluffy coat into many different styles. Being groomed in this way makes the Pokémon both fancier and faster.

FURRET
TYPE: Normal
HEIGHT: 1.8m
WEIGHT: 32.5kg

With its long, thin body and impressive speed, Furret has an evasive edge in battle. It can often wriggle right out of an opponent's grasp.

GABITE
TYPE: Dragon - Ground
HEIGHT: 1.4m
WEIGHT: 56.0kg

While digging to expand its nest, Gabite sometimes finds sparkly gems that then become part of its hoard.

GALLADE
TYPE: Psychic - Fighting
HEIGHT: 1.6m
WEIGHT: 52.0kg

A master of the blade, Gallade battles using the swordlike appendages that extend from its elbows.

GALVANTULA
TYPE: Bug - Electric
HEIGHT: 0.8m
WEIGHT: 14.3kg

Galvantula's webs crackle with electricity, which shocks anything that blunders into them. It can also spin an electric barrier in battle.

GARBODOR
TYPE: Poison
HEIGHT: 1.9m
WEIGHT: 107.3kg

Garbodor wraps its long left arm around an opponent to bring it within range of its poisonous breath. It creates new kinds of poison by eating garbage.

GARCHOMP
TYPE: Dragon - Ground
HEIGHT: 1.9m
WEIGHT: 95.0kg

Garchomp can fly faster than the speed of sound. When it assumes a streamlined position for flight, it looks like a fighter jet.

GARDEVOIR
TYPE: Psychic - Fairy
HEIGHT: 1.6m
WEIGHT: 48.4kg

Fiercely protective of its Trainer, Gardevoir can see into the future to detect a threat to that Trainer. It responds by unleashing the full strength of its psychic powers.

GASTLY
TYPE: Ghost - Poison
HEIGHT: 1.3m
WEIGHT: 0.1kg

Gastly's body is made of gas clouds that can be disrupted by strong winds. Groups of them sometimes huddle close to a house for protection.

GASTRODON
TYPE: Water - Ground
HEIGHT: 0.9m
WEIGHT: 29.9kg

It's said that Gastrodon were once covered by protective shells, but over the ages, those shells have vanished. When threatened, they release purple fluid to cover their escape.

GENESECT
MYTHICAL
TYPE: Bug - Steel
HEIGHT: 1.5m
WEIGHT: 82.5kg

The powerful cannon on Genesect's back is the result of Team Plasma's meddling. This Mythical Pokémon is 300 million years old.

GENGAR
TYPE: Ghost - Poison
HEIGHT: 1.5m
WEIGHT: 40.5kg

If your shadow suddenly runs away, it might be a Gengar stalking you through the darkness.

GEODUDE
TYPE: Water - Rock
HEIGHT: 0.4m
WEIGHT: 20.0kg

As a Geodude grows older, its rough edges are smoothed away. When it sleeps, it digs into the ground, where it resembles a rock.

GIBLE
TYPE: Dragon - Ground
HEIGHT: 0.7m
WEIGHT: 20.5kg

Gible dig holes in the walls of warm caves to make their nests. Don't get too close, or they might pounce!

GIGALITH
TYPE: Rock
HEIGHT: 1.7m
WEIGHT: 260.0kg

After Gigalith soaks up the sun's rays, it uses its energy core to process that energy into a weapon. A blast of its compressed energy can destroy a mountain.

GIRAFARIG
TYPE: Normal - Psychic
HEIGHT: 1.5m
WEIGHT: 41.5kg

The brain that controls Girafarig's secondary head is too small to think and just reacts to its surroundings. It tends to attack anyone who approaches from behind.

GLACEON
TYPE: Ice
HEIGHT: 0.8m
WEIGHT: 25.9kg

The icy Glaceon has amazing control over its body temperature. It can freeze its own fur and then fire the frozen hairs like needles at an opponent.

GLALIE
TYPE: Ice
HEIGHT: 1.5m
WEIGHT: 256.5kg

Glalie's rocky body is surrounded by a sturdy shell of ice, which it creates by freezing water vapor in the air around it. It can also create amazing ice sculptures with this power.

LEGENDARY

GIRATINA

TYPE: Ghost - Dragon	
HEIGHT: 4.5m	
WEIGHT: 750.0kg	

As punishment, the Legendary Pokémon Giratina was banished to another dimension, where everything is distorted and reversed.

GLAMEOW

TYPE: Normal
HEIGHT: 0.5m
WEIGHT: 3.9kg

When it's feeling happy and friendly, Glameow purrs winningly and performs a lovely dance with its spiraling tail. When it's in a bad mood, however, the claws come out.

GLIGAR

TYPE: Ground - Fying
HEIGHT: 1.1m
WEIGHT: 64.8kg

Gliding silently through the air, Gligar can strike from above to grab onto an opponent's face with all four of its claws. The barb on its tail is poisonous.

GLISCOR

TYPE: Ground - Flying
HEIGHT: 2.0m
WEIGHT: 42.5kg

Gliscor hangs upside-down from trees, watching for its chance to attack. At the right moment, it silently swoops, with its long tail ready to seize its opponent.

GLOOM

TYPE: Grass - Poison
HEIGHT: 0.8m
WEIGHT: 8.6kg

Gloom doesn't always smell terrible—when it feels safe and relaxed, its aroma fades. However, its nectar usually carries an awful stench.

GOGOAT

TYPE: Grass
HEIGHT: 1.7m
WEIGHT: 91.0kg

This perceptive Pokémon can read its riders' feelings by paying attention to their grip on its horns. Gogoat also use their horns in battles for leadership.

GOLBAT

TYPE: Poison - Flying
HEIGHT: 1.6m
WEIGHT: 55.0kg

With its four sharp fangs, Golbat feeds on living beings. Darkness gives it an advantage in battle, and it prefers to attack on pitch-black nights.

GOLDEEN

TYPE: Water
HEIGHT: 0.6m
WEIGHT: 15.0kg

Goldeen's long, elegant fins wave gracefully in the water. It's hard to keep this lovely Pokémon in an aquarium, because its horn can break through thick glass.

GOLDUCK

TYPE: Water
HEIGHT: 1.7m
WEIGHT: 76.6kg

The webbing on its legs makes Golduck an excellent swimmer. Even when facing strong currents and towering waves, it can cut through the water to rescue shipwreck victims.

GOLEM

TYPE: Rock - Ground
HEIGHT: 1.4m
WEIGHT: 300.0kg

People who live on mountainsides sometimes dig grooves to keep Golem from rolling right into their houses.

GOLETT

TYPE: Ground - Ghost
HEIGHT: 1.0m
WEIGHT: 92.0kg

Sculpted from clay and animated by a mysterious internal energy, Golett are the product of ancient science.

GOLURK

TYPE: Ground - Ghost
HEIGHT: 2.8m
WEIGHT: 330.0kg

The seal on Golurk's chest keeps its energy contained and stops it from going wild. Long ago, these Pokémon were created as protectors.

GOODRA

TYPE: Dragon
HEIGHT: 2.0m
WEIGHT: 150.5kg

The affectionate Goodra just loves to give its Trainer a big hug! Unfortunately, its hugs leave the recipient covered in goo.

GOOMY

TYPE: Dragon
HEIGHT: 0.3m
WEIGHT: 2.8kg

The slippery membrane that covers Goomy's body deflects the fists and feet of its attackers. To keep itself from drying out, it stays away from the sun.

GOREBYSS

TYPE: Water
HEIGHT: 1.8m
WEIGHT: 22.6kg

Gorebyss is tougher than it looks. Its long, slender body is built to withstand the crushing pressure at the bottom of the ocean. Regular attacks just won't do much.

GOTHITA
TYPE:	Psychic
HEIGHT:	0.4m
WEIGHT:	5.8kg

Gothita's wide eyes are always fixed on something. It seems when they stare like that, they're seeing what others cannot.

GOTHITELLE
TYPE:	Psychic
HEIGHT:	1.5m
WEIGHT:	44.0kg

Gothitelle observes the stars to predict the future. It sometimes distorts the air around itself to reveal faraway constellations.

GOTHORITA
TYPE:	Psychic
HEIGHT:	0.7m
WEIGHT:	18.0kg

Gothorita draw their power from starlight. On starry nights, they can make stones float and control people's movements with their enhanced psychic power.

GOURGEIST
TYPE:	Ghost - Grass
HEIGHT:	0.9m
WEIGHT:	12.5kg

During the new moon, the eerie song of the Gourgeist echoes through town, bringing woe to anyone who hears it.

GRANBULL
TYPE:	Fairy
HEIGHT:	1.4m
WEIGHT:	48.7kg

The weight of the huge fangs in Granbull's lower jaw throw the Pokémon off balance, so it has to walk with its head tilted back. It generally doesn't bite unless startled.

GRAVELER
TYPE:	Rock - Ground
HEIGHT:	1.0m
WEIGHT:	105.0kg

Graveler loves to eat rocks, and moss-covered rocks are a favorite snack. It will munch its way up the side of a mountain if it's hungry.

GRENINJA
TYPE:	Water - Dark
HEIGHT:	1.5m
WEIGHT:	40.0kg

Greninja can compress water into sharp-edged throwing stars. With the grace of a ninja, it slips in and out of sight to attack from the shadows.

GRIMER
TYPE:	Poison
HEIGHT:	0.9m
WEIGHT:	30.0kg

Because its body is like sludge, Grimer can squeeze itself into small openings like sewer pipes. The fluid it gives off is full of germs.

LEGENDARY

GROUDON
TYPE:	Ground
HEIGHT:	3.5m
WEIGHT:	950.0kg

Legends say that Groudon is the land personified. When it channels the full power of nature, it can expand the landmass with eruptions of magma. This Pokémon often clashes with Kyogre.

GROTLE
TYPE:	Grass
HEIGHT:	1.1m
WEIGHT:	97.0kg

Grotle leaves the shade of its forest home to soak up sunlight with its shell. It's good at finding clear water, and smaller Pokémon often ride on its back when they're thirsty.

GROVYLE
TYPE:	Grass
HEIGHT:	0.9m
WEIGHT:	21.6kg

Grovyle can travel so swiftly from branch to branch that it looks like it's flying through the forest. The leaves on its body are excellent camouflage.

GROWLITHE
TYPE:	Fire
HEIGHT:	0.7m
WEIGHT:	19.0kg

Growlithe has an excellent nose and a good memory for scents. It can even sniff out people's emotions.

GRUMPIG
TYPE:	Psychic
HEIGHT:	0.9m
WEIGHT:	71.5kg

Grumpig breaks into a strange dance when it's using its black pearls to focus its psychic power. Many collectors consider the pearls to be priceless artwork.

GULPIN
TYPE:	Poison
HEIGHT:	0.4m
WEIGHT:	10.3kg

Gulpin's stomach takes up most of its body, so there's not much room for its other organs. Its powerful digestive enzymes make short work of anything it swallows.

GURDURR
TYPE:	Fighting
HEIGHT:	1.2m
WEIGHT:	40.0kg

With its strong muscles, Gurdurr can wield its steel beam with ease in battle. It's so sturdy that a whole team of wrestlers couldn't knock it down.

GYARADOS
TYPE:	Water - Flying
HEIGHT:	6.5m
WEIGHT:	235.0kg

After evolving, Gyarados experiences a shift in the cellular structure of its brain. This may explain why it is so violent, sometimes going on monthlong rampages.

HAPPINY
TYPE:	Normal
HEIGHT:	0.6m
WEIGHT:	24.4kg

In the pouch on its belly, Happiny carefully stores a round, white stone that resembles an egg. It sometimes offers this stone to those it likes.

HARIYAMA
TYPE:	Fighting
HEIGHT:	2.3m
WEIGHT:	253.8kg

Don't let Hariyama's bulk fool you – it's made of pure muscle. A single strike from its open palm can snap a thick tree in half.

HAUNTER
TYPE:	Ghost - Poison
HEIGHT:	1.6m
WEIGHT:	0.1kg

Don't ever let a Haunter lick you! Its ghostly tongue can steal your life energy.

HAWLUCHA
TYPE:	Fighting - Flying
HEIGHT:	0.8m
WEIGHT:	21.5kg

Hawlucha prefers to fight by diving at its foes from above. This aerial advantage makes up for its small size.

HAXORUS
TYPE:	Dragon
HEIGHT:	1.8m
WEIGHT:	105.5kg

Haxorus can cut through steel with its mighty tusks, which stay sharp no matter what. Its body is heavily armored.

HEATMOR
TYPE:	Fire
HEIGHT:	1.4m
WEIGHT:	58.0kg

Heatmor can control the flame from its mouth like a tongue, and the fire is so hot that it can melt through steel. Heatmor and Durant are natural enemies.

LEGENDARY

HEATRAN
TYPE: Fire - Steel		Heatran makes its home in caves carved
HEIGHT: 1.7m		out by volcanic eruptions. This Legendary Pokémon's feet can dig into rock,
WEIGHT: 430.0kg		allowing it to walk on walls and ceilings.

HELIOLISK
TYPE:	Electric - Normal
HEIGHT:	1.0m
WEIGHT:	21.0kg

Heliolisk generates electricity by spreading its frill out wide to soak up the sun. It uses this energy to boost its speed.

HELIOPTILE
TYPE:	Electric - Normal
HEIGHT:	0.5m
WEIGHT:	6.0kg

The frills on Helioptile's head soak up sunlight and create electricity. In this way, they can generate enough energy to keep them going without food.

HERACROSS
TYPE:	Bug - Fighting
HEIGHT:	1.5m
WEIGHT:	54.0kg

Though its feet end in sharp claws, Heracross doesn't use them as a weapon. Instead, it digs them into the ground to brace itself while it uses its giant horn to scoop up an enemy.

LEGENDARY

HO-OH
TYPE: Fire - Flying		When Ho-Oh's feathers catch the light at
HEIGHT: 3.8m		different angles, they glow in a rainbow of colors. Legend says these feathers
WEIGHT: 199.0kg		bring joy to whoever holds one.

HERDIER
TYPE:	Normal
HEIGHT:	0.9m
WEIGHT:	14.7kg

Herdier is known for its unwavering loyalty, even helping its Trainer take care of other Pokémon. The black fur on its back protects it like a cape.

HIPPOPOTAS
TYPE:	Ground
HEIGHT:	0.8m
WEIGHT:	49.5kg

Hippopotas lives in a dry environment. Its body gives off sand instead of sweat, and this sandy shield keeps it protected from water and germs.

HIPPOWDON
TYPE:	Ground
HEIGHT:	2.0m
WEIGHT:	300.0kg

Hippowdon stores sand inside its body and expels it through the ports on its sides to create a twisting sandstorm in battle.

HITMONCHAN
TYPE:	Fighting
HEIGHT:	1.4m
WEIGHT:	50.2kg

Hitmonchan has the fighting spirit of a world-class boxer. It's extremely driven and never gives up.

HITMONLEE
TYPE:	Fighting
HEIGHT:	1.5m
WEIGHT:	49.8kg

Hitmonlee can extend its legs like springs to deliver kicks with tremendous force. It's always careful to stretch and loosen up after battle.

HITMONTOP
TYPE:	Fighting
HEIGHT:	1.4m
WEIGHT:	48.0kg

Hitmontop's spinning kicks balance offense and defense. Walking is a less efficient mode of travel for it than spinning.

HONCHKROW
TYPE: Dark - Flying
HEIGHT: 0.9m
WEIGHT: 27.3kg

When Honchkrow cries out in its deep voice, several Murkrow will appear to answer the call. It's most active after dark.

HONEDGE
TYPE: Steel - Ghost
HEIGHT: 0.8m
WEIGHT: 2.0kg

Beware when approaching a Honedge! Those foolish enough to wield it like a sword will quickly find themselves wrapped in its blue cloth and drained of energy.

MYTHICAL

HOOPA
TYPE: Psychic - Ghost
HEIGHT: 0.9m
WEIGHT: 5.0kg

According to myth, Hoopa can summon whatever it wants with the enormous power of its six rings. When that power is confined, it is much smaller and less destructive.

HOOTHOOT
TYPE: Normal - Flying
HEIGHT: 0.7m
WEIGHT: 21.2kg

Hoothoot has a special sense organ that allows it to track the rotation of the planet. It always starts to hoot at the same time of day, and this timing is so exact you could set your watch by it.

HOPPIP
TYPE: Grass - Flying
HEIGHT: 0.4m
WEIGHT: 0.5kg

Since Hoppip floats on the wind, it must cluster together with others to withstand strong gusts. Otherwise, it might be blown away!

HORSEA
TYPE: Water
HEIGHT: 0.4m
WEIGHT: 8.0kg

Horsea wraps its tail around solid objects on the seafloor to avoid being swept away in a strong current. When threatened, it spits a cloud of ink to cover its escape.

HOUNDOOM
TYPE: Dark - Fire
HEIGHT: 1.4m
WEIGHT: 35.0kg

Houndoom choose who will lead their pack by engaging in fierce battles. You can often identify a pack leader by its sharply angled horns.

HOUNDOUR
TYPE: Dark - Fire
HEIGHT: 0.6m
WEIGHT: 10.8kg

Houndour are known for their teamwork. They hunt in packs and use different kinds of cries to coordinate their group attacks.

HUNTAIL
TYPE: Water
HEIGHT: 1.7m
WEIGHT: 27.0kg

Huntail lives in the darkest depths of the sea, so people didn't know about it for a long time. Its tail, which resembles a small creature, sometimes tricks others into attacking.

HYDREIGON
TYPE: Dark - Dragon
HEIGHT: 1.8m
WEIGHT: 160.0kg

The smaller heads on Hydreigon's arms don't have brains, but they can still eat. Any movement within its line of sight will be greeted with a frightening attack.

HYPNO
TYPE: Psychic
HEIGHT: 1.6m
WEIGHT: 75.6kg

As Hypno's pendulum swings and shines, anyone watching falls into a hypnotic trance. To enhance the effect, it always keeps the pendulum polished.

IGGLYBUFF
TYPE: Normal - Fairy
HEIGHT: 0.3m
WEIGHT: 1.0kg

Before it evolves, Igglybuff's vocal cords are underdeveloped, and singing hurts its throat. Its soft, squishy body gives off a sweet, calming aroma.

ILLUMISE
TYPE: Bug
HEIGHT: 0.6m
WEIGHT: 17.7kg

Illumise gives off a sweet scent that attracts Volbeat by the dozen. Then, it directs the swarm in drawing patterns of light across the night sky.

INFERNAPE
TYPE: Fire - Fighting
HEIGHT: 1.2m
WEIGHT: 55.0kg

Swift and agile, Infernape puts all four of its limbs to use in its distinctive fighting style. The fire on its head mirrors the fire in its spirit.

INKAY
TYPE: Dark - Psychic
HEIGHT: 0.4m
WEIGHT: 3.5kg

The spots on Inkay's body emit a flashing light. This light confuses its opponents, giving it a chance to escape.

IVYSAUR
TYPE: Grass - Poison
HEIGHT: 1.0m
WEIGHT: 13.0kg

Carrying the weight of the bud on its back makes Ivysaur's legs stronger. When the bud is close to blooming, the Pokémon spends more time sleeping in the sun.

JELLICENT
TYPE: Water - Ghost
HEIGHT: 2.2m
WEIGHT: 135.0kg

Though most of its body is made of seawater, Jellicent should not be underestimated. Stories tell of a whole fleet of shipwrecks on the floor of its ocean home.

MYTHICAL

JIRACHI
TYPE: Steel - Psychic
HEIGHT: 0.3m
WEIGHT: 1.1kg

According to myth, if you write your wish on one of the notes attached to Jirachi's head and then sing to it in a pure voice, the Pokémon will awaken from its thousand-year slumber and grant your wish.

JIGGLYPUFF
TYPE: Normal - Fairy
HEIGHT: 0.5m
WEIGHT: 5.5kg

Jigglypuff's primary weapon is its song, which lulls opponents to sleep. Because it never stops to breathe while singing, long battles can put it in danger.

JOLTEON
TYPE: Electric
HEIGHT: 0.8m
WEIGHT: 24.5kg

Jolteon's fur carries a static charge, and its body generates electricity. It can channel this electricity during battle to call down a thunderbolt!

JOLTIK
TYPE: Bug - Electric
HEIGHT: 0.1m
WEIGHT: 0.6kg

Joltik can't produce their own electricity, so they attach to larger Pokémon and suck up the static electricity given off. They store this energy in a special pouch.

JUMPLUFF
TYPE: Grass - Flying
HEIGHT: 0.8m
WEIGHT: 3.0kg

If Jumpluff hits a patch of cold air while it's drifting on the wind, it will return to the ground to await a warm breeze. The winds carry its fluffy body across the sea and around the world.

JYNX
TYPE: Ice - Psychic
HEIGHT: 1.4m
WEIGHT: 40.6kg

Jynx has a hypnotic, rhythmic walk that makes it look like it's dancing. People who watch it move often find themselves dancing along.

KABUTO
TYPE: Rock - Water
HEIGHT: 0.5m
WEIGHT: 11.5kg

Kabuto has remained unchanged for 300 million years. It was restored from a fossil, but every once in a while, a living specimen is discovered in the wild.

KABUTOPS
TYPE: Rock - Water
HEIGHT: 1.3m
WEIGHT: 40.5kg

Long ago, Kabutops swam through ancient seas in search of food. Its legs and gills were just beginning to adapt to a life on land.

KADABRA
TYPE: Psychic
HEIGHT: 1.3m
WEIGHT: 56.5kg

The silver spoon Kadabra carries intensifies its brain waves. Only those with strong minds should attempt to train this Pokémon.

KAKUNA
TYPE: Bug - Poison
HEIGHT: 0.6m
WEIGHT: 10.0kg

Kakuna appears motionless from the outside, but inside its shell, it's busily preparing to evolve. Sometimes the shell heats up from this activity.

KANGASKHAN
TYPE: Normal
HEIGHT: 2.2m
WEIGHT: 80.0kg

A little Kangaskhan playing on its own should be left alone. The Parent Pokémon always keeps careful watch and will attack any aggressor.

KARRABLAST
TYPE: Bug
HEIGHT: 0.5m
WEIGHT: 5.9kg

Karrablast often attack Shelmet, trying to steal their shells. When electrical energy envelops them at the same time, they both evolve.

KECLEON
TYPE: Normal
HEIGHT: 1.0m
WEIGHT: 22.0kg

Kecleon is a master of camouflage and can change the color of its skin to hide in any environment. However, its zigzag pattern is always the same.

MYTHICAL

KELDEO
TYPE: Water - Fighting
HEIGHT: 1.4m
WEIGHT: 48.5kg

Keldeo travels the world visiting beaches and riverbanks, where it can race across the water. When this Mythical Pokémon is filled with resolve, it gains a blinding speed.

KINGDRA
TYPE: Water - Dragon
HEIGHT: 1.8m
WEIGHT: 152.0kg

Kingdra makes its home so deep in the ocean that nothing else lives there. Some people think its yawn influences the currents.

KINGLER
TYPE: Water
HEIGHT: 1.3m
WEIGHT: 60.0kg

When one Kingler waves to another with its giant claw, it's sending a message. They can't hold long conversations this way, though, because waving those heavy claws is tiring.

KIRLIA
TYPE: Psychic - Fairy
HEIGHT: 0.8m
WEIGHT: 20.2kg

A Kirlia whose Trainer has a positive attitude develops a shining beauty. When this Pokémon uses its psychic powers, strange mirages surround it.

KLANG
TYPE: Steel
HEIGHT: 0.6m
WEIGHT: 51.0kg

Klang's body is made up of one minigear and one bigger gear, which change their rotation to communicate with other Klang. It can shoot the minigear at an opponent in battle.

KLEFKI
TYPE: Steel - Fairy
HEIGHT: 0.2m
WEIGHT: 3.0kg

To keep valuables locked up tight, give the key to a Klefki. This Pokémon loves to collect keys, and it will guard its collection with all its might.

KLINK
TYPE: Steel
HEIGHT: 0.3m
WEIGHT: 21.0kg

The two minigears that make up Klink's body are meant for each other. If they get separated, they won't mesh with any other minigear until they find each other again.

KLINKLANG
TYPE: Steel
HEIGHT: 0.6m
WEIGHT: 81.0kg

Klinklang stores energy in its red core and charges itself up by spinning that gear rapidly. It can shoot the energy from the spikes on its outer ring.

KOFFING
TYPE: Poison
HEIGHT: 0.6m
WEIGHT: 1.0kg

The gases that fill Koffing's body are extremely toxic. When it's under attack, it releases this poisonous gas from jets on its surface.

KRABBY
TYPE: Water
HEIGHT: 0.4m
WEIGHT: 6.5kg

Krabby dig holes in sandy beaches to make their homes. When the food supply is limited, they sometimes fight over territory.

KRICKETOT
TYPE: Bug
HEIGHT: 0.3m
WEIGHT: 2.2kg

The sound of Kricketot's antennae knocking together resembles the sound of a xylophone. They use these sounds to communicate.

KRICKETUNE
TYPE: Bug
HEIGHT: 1.0m
WEIGHT: 22.5kg

Kricketune composes many different melodies that reflect its emotional state. Researchers are trying to determine whether the patterns of its music have a deeper meaning.

KROKOROK
TYPE: Ground - Dark
HEIGHT: 1.0m
WEIGHT: 33.4kg

The membranes that cover Krokorok's eyes not only protect the eyes during sandstorms, but also act like heat sensors, enabling it to navigate in total darkness.

KROOKODILE
TYPE: Ground - Dark
HEIGHT: 1.5m
WEIGHT: 96.3kg

Krookodile's formidable jaws are capable of crunching up cars. Triggered into violence by nearby movement, Krookodile will clamp on inescapably with all the might of those jaws.

LEGENDARY

KYOGRE
TYPE: Water
HEIGHT: 4.5m
WEIGHT: 352.0kg

Legends say that Kyogre is the sea personified. When it channels the full power of nature, it can raise sea levels with mighty storms. This Pokémon often clashes with Groudon.

LEGENDARY

KYUREM
TYPE: Dragon - Ice
HEIGHT: 3.0m
WEIGHT: 325.0kg

When the freezing energy inside Kyurem leaked out, its entire body froze. Legends say it will become whole with the help of a hero who will bring truth or ideals.

LAIRON
TYPE: Steel - Rock
HEIGHT: 0.9m
WEIGHT: 120.0kg

Lairon lives near tasty, mineral-rich springs, where it tempers its body with iron from the water and rocks. It sometimes comes into conflict with miners going after the same iron ore it uses as a food source.

LEGENDARY

LANDORUS
TYPE: Ground - Flying
HEIGHT: 1.5m
WEIGHT: 68.0kg

Because its arrival helps crops grow, Landorus is welcomed as "The Guardian of the Fields." This Legendary Pokémon uses the energy of wind and lightning to enrich the soil.

LAMPENT
TYPE: Grass - Fire
HEIGHT: 0.6m
WEIGHT: 13.0kg

Lampent tends to lurk grimly around hospitals, waiting for someone to take a bad turn so it can absorb the departing spirit. The stolen spirits keep its fire burning.

LANTURN
TYPE: Water - Electric
HEIGHT: 1.2m
WEIGHT: 22.5kg

Lanturn's antenna produces a light bright enough to be seen from the surface when it's swimming deep in the ocean. Its nickname is "the deep-sea star."

LAPRAS
TYPE: Water - Ice
HEIGHT: 2.2m
WEIGHT: 220.0kg

When a Lapras sings a sad song at twilight, it's said to be looking for other Lapras. Because of human activity, these Pokémon are growing more rare.

LARVESTA
TYPE: Bug - Fire
HEIGHT: 1.1m
WEIGHT: 28.8kg

From its five horns, Larvesta sends out flames to keep attackers at bay. When it's ready to evolve, it spins a fiery cocoon.

LARVITAR
TYPE: Rock - Ground
HEIGHT: 0.6m
WEIGHT: 72.0kg

Larvitar hatches from an egg buried deep underground. It has to eat its way to the surface by devouring the soil above it.

LOTAD
TYPE: Water - Grass
HEIGHT: 0.5m
WEIGHT: 2.6kg

The leaf on Lotad's head is too big and heavy for it to carry on land, so it floats on the surface of the water.

LOUDRED
TYPE: Normal
HEIGHT: 1.0m
WEIGHT: 40.5kg

Loudred shouts at such volume that it temporarily deafens itself. The sound waves it produces can knock down a wooden house.

LUCARIO
TYPE: Fighting - Steel
HEIGHT: 1.2m
WEIGHT: 54.0kg

Sensing the auras that all beings emanate allows Lucario to read their minds and predict their movements. It is also very sensitive to others' emotions.

LUDICOLO
TYPE: Water - Grass
HEIGHT: 1.5m
WEIGHT: 55.0kg

Ludicolo just can't help leaping into a joyful dance when it hears a festive tune. Children who sing while hiking often attract its attention.

LUMINEON
TYPE: Water
HEIGHT: 1.2m
WEIGHT: 24.0kg

Lumineon lives at the bottom of the deep blue sea. The patterns on its tail give off light, and it can use its front fins to crawl along the sand unnoticed.

LEGENDARY

LUGIA
TYPE: Psychic - Flying
HEIGHT: 5.2m
WEIGHT: 216.0kg

Lugia can knock down a house with one flutter of its enormously powerful wings. For the safety of others, this Legendary Pokémon lives at the bottom of the sea.

LUNATONE
TYPE: Rock - Psychic
HEIGHT: 1.0m
WEIGHT: 168.0kg

People think Lunatone came from space, because it was first discovered near a meteorite. It floats to get around instead of walking, and its red eyes can freeze a foe with fear.

LUVDISC
TYPE: Water
HEIGHT: 0.6m
WEIGHT: 8.7kg

Because of its pink, heart-shaped body and its habit of swimming around affectionate couples in shallow tropical seas, Luvdisc is considered a symbol of romance.

LUXIO
TYPE: Electirc
HEIGHT: 0.9m
WEIGHT: 30.5kg

A powerful electric current arcs between Luxio's claws, making it a dangerous opponent in battle. They form small groups and live together.

LUXRAY
TYPE: Electric
HEIGHT: 1.4m
WEIGHT: 42.0kg

Luxray's gleaming golden eyes can see right through solid objects. This is very useful when it's keeping watch for approaching threats or looking for food.

MACHAMP
TYPE: Fighting
HEIGHT: 1.6m
WEIGHT: 130.0kg

Though it is a master of martial arts, Machamp sometimes gets its four arms tangled up when trying to do more intricate tasks.

MACHOKE
TYPE: Fighting
HEIGHT: 1.5m
WEIGHT: 70.5kg

Machoke never stop training. Even when they have jobs helping people with heavy labor, they spend their free time building up their muscles.

MACHOP
TYPE: Fighting
HEIGHT: 0.8m
WEIGHT: 19.5kg

Machop lifts a Graveler like a weight to make its muscles stronger. No matter how much it exercises, it never gets sore.

MAGBY
TYPE: Fire
HEIGHT: 0.7m
WEIGHT: 21.4kg

A Magby that's breathing yellow flames is a healthy Magby. If the flames are smoking and sputtering, it probably needs to get some rest.

MAGCARGO
TYPE: Fire - Rock
HEIGHT: 0.8m
WEIGHT: 55.0kg

Magcargo's body is so hot that it vaporizes any nearby water. When the weather turns rainy, Magcargo is surrounded by a thick cloud of steam.

MAGIKARP
TYPE: Water
HEIGHT: 0.9m
WEIGHT: 10.0kg

Though Magikarp is an exceptionally weak Pokémon when it comes to battle skills, it has an extremely strong constitution. It can live in the most polluted of water.

MAGMAR
TYPE: Fire
HEIGHT: 1.3m
WEIGHT: 44.5kg

When Magmar releases bursts of flame during a battle, any nearby plant life is in danger of catching fire.

MAGMORTAR
TYPE: Fire
HEIGHT: 1.6m
WEIGHT: 68.0kg

Magmortar makes its home inside a volcano's crater. Its breath is searingly hot, as are the fireballs it blasts out of its arms.

MAGNEMITE
TYPE: Electric - Steel
HEIGHT: 0.3m
WEIGHT: 6.0kg

A sudden power failure can sometimes be traced to many Magnemite draining energy from the power lines that feed a building.

MAGNETON
TYPE: Electric - Steel
HEIGHT: 1.0m
WEIGHT: 60.0kg

The magnetic field that surrounds Magneton can wreak havoc on electronics and other machines. Having this Pokémon around can be very bad for business.

MAGNEZONE
TYPE: Electric - Steel
HEIGHT: 1.2m
WEIGHT: 180.0kg

Magnezone give off a strong magnetic field that they can't always control. Sometimes they attract each other by accident and stick so tightly that they have trouble separating.

MAKUHITA
TYPE: Fighting
HEIGHT: 1.0m
WEIGHT: 86.4kg

If the tireless Makuhita gets knocked down in battle, it always gets up again. Every time it does so, it builds up energy for Evolution.

MALAMAR
TYPE: Dark - Psychic
HEIGHT: 1.5m
WEIGHT: 47.0kg

With hypnotic compulsion, Malamar can control the actions of others, forcing them to do its will. The movement of its tentacles can put anyone watching into a trance.

MAMOSWINE
TYPE: Ice - Ground
HEIGHT: 2.5m
WEIGHT: 291.0kg

Mamoswine have been around since the last ice age, but the warmer climate reduced their population. Their huge twin tusks are formed of ice.

MANAPHY
MYTHICAL
TYPE: Water
HEIGHT: 0.3m
WEIGHT: 1.4kg

From its earliest days, Manaphy possesses the power to form close bonds with any Pokémon, no matter what kind.

MANDIBUZZ
TYPE: Dark - Flying
HEIGHT: 1.2m
WEIGHT: 39.5kg

Mandibuzz flies in slow circles, high in the sky, to keep an eye out for a weak opponent. Then it swoops down in an aerial attack.

MANECTRIC
TYPE: Electric
HEIGHT: 1.5m
WEIGHT: 40.2kg

When Manectric enters battle, thunderclouds follow. Its mane gives off a strong electric charge.

MANKEY
TYPE: Fighting
HEIGHT: 0.5m
WEIGHT: 28.0kg

Mankey flies into a rage at the slightest provocation. These fits of temper are usually preceded by violent tremors, but there's rarely enough time to get away.

MANTINE
TYPE: Water - Flying
HEIGHT: 2.1m
WEIGHT: 220.0kg

When the weather is nice, Mantine often leap gracefully out of the waves into the bright sunlight. Sometimes Remoraid go along for the ride.

MANTYKE
TYPE: Water - Flying
HEIGHT: 1.0m
WEIGHT: 65.0kg

Mantyke that live in different regions have different patterns on their backs. They're often found in the company of Remoraid.

MARACTUS
TYPE: Grass
HEIGHT: 1.0m
WEIGHT: 28.0kg

Maractus live in dry places, where they dance with rhythmic movements of their prickly limbs to keep others away. This motion gives off a sound like the shaking of maracas.

MAREEP
TYPE: Electric
HEIGHT: 0.6m
WEIGHT: 7.8kg

When Mareep's woolly coat builds up static electricity, the end of its tail glows brightly. The static charge grows as Mareep moves and its wool rubs together.

MARILL
TYPE: Water - Fairy
HEIGHT: 0.4m
WEIGHT: 8.5kg

When Marill dives underwater in search of plants to eat, its buoyant tail bobs on the surface. The tail is flexible enough to wrap around a tree as an anchor.

MAROWAK
TYPE: Ground
HEIGHT: 1.0m
WEIGHT: 45.0kg

After overcoming its grief and evolving, Marowak has become extremely tough. Its spirit, tempered by adversity, can withstand just about anything.

MARSHTOMP
TYPE: Water - Ground
HEIGHT: 0.7m
WEIGHT: 28.0kg

When the tide goes out, Marshtomp loves to play in the mud. Its well-developed hind legs offer stability, so it can travel over mud faster than it can swim.

MASQUERAIN
TYPE: Bug - Flying
HEIGHT: 0.8m
WEIGHT: 3.6kg

The eye patterns on Masquerain's large antennae usually have an angry expression, which sometimes scares would-be opponents. If the eyes look sad, it's a sign that heavy rain is coming.

MAWILE
TYPE: Steel - Fairy
HEIGHT: 0.6m
WEIGHT: 11.5kg

An enemy fooled by Mawile's sweet face will quickly find itself in the crushing grip of the massive steel jaws on the back of this Pokémon's head.

MEDICHAM
TYPE: Fighting - Psychic
HEIGHT: 1.3m
WEIGHT: 31.5kg

Medicham has developed a sixth sense and psychic powers through long meditation training. It can disappear into its mountain home if danger approaches.

MEDITITE
TYPE: Fighting - Psychic
HEIGHT: 0.6m
WEIGHT: 11.2kg

Through intense meditation and extreme hunger, Meditite works hard to train its mental powers.

MEGA ABOMASNOW
TYPE: Grass - Ice
HEIGHT: 2.7m
WEIGHT: 185.0kg

MEGA ABSOL
TYPE: Dark
HEIGHT: 1.2m
WEIGHT: 49.0kg

MEGA AERODACTYL
TYPE: Rock - Flying
HEIGHT: 2.1m
WEIGHT: 79.0kg

MEGA AGGRON
TYPE: Steel | HEIGHT: 2.2m | WEIGHT: 395.0kg

MEGA ALAKAZAM
TYPE: Psychic
HEIGHT: 1.2m
WEIGHT: 48.0kg

MEGA ALTARIA
TYPE: Dragon - Fairy
HEIGHT: 1.5m
WEIGHT: 20.6kg

MEGA AMPHAROS
TYPE: Electric - Dragon
HEIGHT: 1.4m
WEIGHT: 61.5kg

MEGA AUDINO
TYPE: Normal - Fairy
HEIGHT: 1.5m
WEIGHT: 32.0kg

MEGA BANETTE
TYPE: Ghost
HEIGHT: 1.2m
WEIGHT: 13.0kg

MEGA BEEDRILL
TYPE: Bug - Poison
HEIGHT: 1.4m
WEIGHT: 40.5kg

MEGA CAMERUPT
TYPE: Fire - Ground
HEIGHT: 2.5m
WEIGHT: 320.5kg

MEGA CHARIZARD X
TYPE: Fire - Dragon
HEIGHT: 1.7m
WEIGHT: 110.5kg

MEGA BLASTOISE
TYPE: Water
HEIGHT: 1.6m
WEIGHT: 101.1kg

MEGA BLAZIKEN
TYPE: Fire - Fighting | HEIGHT: 1.9m | WEIGHT: 52.0kg

MEGA CHARIZARD Y
TYPE: Fire - Flying
HEIGHT: 1.7m
WEIGHT: 100.5kg

MEGA DIANCIE
TYPE: Rock - Fairy
HEIGHT: 1.1m
WEIGHT: 27.8kg

MEGA GALLADE

TYPE: Psychic - Fighting	
HEIGHT: 1.6m	
WEIGHT: 56.4kg	

MEGA GARCHOMP

TYPE: Dragon - Ground	
HEIGHT: 1.9m	
WEIGHT: 95.0kg	

MEGA GARDEVOIR

TYPE: Psychic - Fairy	
HEIGHT: 1.6m	
WEIGHT: 48.4kg	

MEGA GENGAR

TYPE: Ghost - Poison	
HEIGHT: 1.4m	
WEIGHT: 40.5kg	

MEGA GLALIE

TYPE: Ice	
HEIGHT: 2.1m	
WEIGHT: 350.2kg	

MEGA GYARADOS

TYPE: Water - Dark	
HEIGHT: 6.5m	
WEIGHT: 305.0 kg	

MEGA HERACROSS

TYPE: Bug - Fighting	
HEIGHT: 1.7m	
WEIGHT: 62.5kg	

MEGA KANGASKHAN

TYPE: Normal	
HEIGHT: 2.2m	
WEIGHT: 100.0kg	

MEGA LATIAS

TYPE: Dragon - Psychic	
HEIGHT: 1.8m	
WEIGHT: 52.0kg	

MEGA LOPUNNY

TYPE: Normal - Fighting	
HEIGHT: 1.3m	
WEIGHT: 28.3kg	

MEGA HOUNDOOM

TYPE: Dark - Fire	HEIGHT: 1.9m	WEIGHT: 49.5kg

MEGA LUCARIO

TYPE: Fighting - Steel	
HEIGHT: 1.3m	
WEIGHT: 57.5kg	

MEGA LATIOS

TYPE: Dragon - Psychic	HEIGHT: 2.3m	WEIGHT: 70.0kg

MEGA MANECTRIC

TYPE: Electric	
HEIGHT: 1.8m	
WEIGHT: 44.0kg	

MEGA MAWILE

TYPE: Steel - Fairy	
HEIGHT: 1.0m	
WEIGHT: 23.5kg	

MEGA MEDICHAM

TYPE: Fighting - Psychic	
HEIGHT: 1.3m	
WEIGHT: 31.5kg	

MEGA METAGROSS
TYPE: Steel - Psychic
HEIGHT: 2.5m
WEIGHT: 942.9kg

MEGA PIDGEOT
TYPE: Normal - Flying
HEIGHT: 2.2m
WEIGHT: 50.5kg

MEGA MEWTWO Y
TYPE: Psychic
HEIGHT: 1.5m
WEIGHT: 33.0kg

MEGA PINSIR
TYPE: Bug - Flying
HEIGHT: 1.7m
WEIGHT: 59.0kg

MEGA RAYQUAZA
TYPE: Dragon - Flying
HEIGHT: 10.8m
WEIGHT: 392.0kg

MEGA SABLEYE
TYPE: Dark - Ghost
HEIGHT: 0.5m
WEIGHT: 11.0kg

MEGA MEWTWO X
TYPE: Psychic - Fighting | HEIGHT: 2.3m | WEIGHT: 127.0kg

MEGA SALAMENCE
TYPE: Dragon - Flying
HEIGHT: 1.8m
WEIGHT: 112.6kg

MEGA SCEPTILE
TYPE: Grass - Dragon
HEIGHT: 1.9m
WEIGHT: 55.2kg

MEGA SCIZOR
TYPE: Bug - Steel
HEIGHT: 2.0m
WEIGHT: 125.0kg

MEGA SHARPEDO
TYPE: Water - Dark
HEIGHT: 2.5m
WEIGHT: 130.3kg

MEGA SLOWBRO
TYPE: Water - Psychic
HEIGHT: 2.0m
WEIGHT: 120.0kg

MEGA STEELIX
TYPE: Steel - Ground
HEIGHT: 10.5 m
WEIGHT: 740.0 kg

MEGA SWAMPERT
TYPE: Water - Ground | HEIGHT: 1.9m | WEIGHT: 102.0kg

MEGA VENUSAUR
TYPE: Grass - Poison
HEIGHT: 2.4m
WEIGHT: 155.5kg

MEGA TYRANITAR
TYPE: Rock - Dark
HEIGHT: 2.5m
WEIGHT: 255.0kg

MEGANIUM
TYPE: Grass
HEIGHT: 1.8m
WEIGHT: 100.5kg

Meganium's flower wafts a soothing aroma. During a battle, the fragrance grows stronger as this Pokémon attempts to calm its enemies.

MYTHICAL

MELOETTA
TYPE: Normal - Psychic
HEIGHT: 0.6m
WEIGHT: 6.5kg

When Meloetta sings, its voice can control the emotions of people or Pokémon. The beautiful melodies of this Mythical Pokémon can bring aching sadness or radiant joy.

MEOWSTIC
TYPE: Psychic
HEIGHT: 0.6m
WEIGHT: 8.5kg

When Meowstic unfolds its ears, the psychic blast created by the eyeball patterns inside can pulverize heavy machinery. It keeps its ears tightly folded unless it's in danger.

MEOWTH
TYPE: Normal
HEIGHT: 0.4m
WEIGHT: 4.2kg

When Meowth retracts its sharp claws, it can move without making a sound or leaving a footprint. It's drawn to shiny things like coins.

LEGENDARY

MESPRIT
TYPE: Psychic
HEIGHT: 0.3m
WEIGHT: 0.3kg

According to legend, Mesprit brought the first taste of joy and sorrow to people's hearts. It is known as "The Being of Emotion."

METAGROSS
TYPE: Steel - Psychic
HEIGHT: 1.6m
WEIGHT: 555.0kg

Metagross is formed when two Metang combine, linking their four brains together. It is intimidating both physically and mentally—it can easily pin a foe underneath its massive steel body and perform complicated calculations in the blink of an eye.

METANG
TYPE: Steel - Psychic
HEIGHT: 1.2m
WEIGHT: 202.5kg

Metang is formed when two Beldum combine, linking their brains and bodies. The power of its linked brains makes it capable of psychokinesis.

METAPOD
TYPE: Bug
HEIGHT: 0.7m
WEIGHT: 9.9kg

Inside its iron-hard shell, Metapod patiently prepares to evolve. It doesn't move much, so it relies on its shell for protection.

MIENFOO
TYPE: Fighting
HEIGHT: 0.9m
WEIGHT: 20.0kg

In battle, Mienfoo never stops moving, flowing through one attack after another with grace and speed. Its claws are very sharp.

MYTHICAL

MEW
TYPE: Psychic
HEIGHT: 0.4m
WEIGHT: 40.0kg

It is said that within Mew's cells rests the entirety of the Pokémon genetic code. This Mythical Pokémon can turn invisible to keep others from noticing it.

LEGENDARY

MEWTWO
TYPE: Psychic
HEIGHT: 2.0m
WEIGHT: 122.0kg

Scientists created Mewtwo by manipulating its genes. If only they could have given it a sense of compassion...

MIENSHAO
TYPE: Fighting
HEIGHT: 1.4m
WEIGHT: 35.5kg

With the long, whiplike fur on its arms, Mienshao can unleash a flurry of attacks so fast they're almost invisible. Its battle combos are unstoppable.

MIGHTYENA
TYPE: Fighting
HEIGHT: 1.0m
WEIGHT: 37.0kg

Mightyena sounds a deep growl before attacking. In the wild, these Pokémon live together in packs.

MILOTIC
TYPE: Water
HEIGHT: 6.2m
WEIGHT: 162.0kg

The astoundingly beautiful Milotic live on lake bottoms and radiate calming energy. When they give off a bright pink glow, people stop fighting.

MILTANK
TYPE: Normal
HEIGHT: 1.2m
WEIGHT: 75.5kg

Miltank produces more than five gallons of milk every day! The milk has a sweet flavor that people of all ages enjoy.

MIME JR.
TYPE: Psychic - Fairy
HEIGHT: 0.6m
WEIGHT: 13.0kg

To enthrall and confuse an attacker, Mime Jr. copies its movements. While the opponent is bewildered, it makes its escape.

MINCCINO
TYPE:	Normal
HEIGHT:	0.4m
WEIGHT:	5.8kg

The very tidy Minccino uses its tail as a broom to rid its habitat of any wayward dust or dirt. They even groom each other with their tails.

MINUN
TYPE:	Electric
HEIGHT:	0.4m
WEIGHT:	4.2kg

Minun shoots out sparks when cheering on its teammates. If the battle isn't going well, the spark showers get more intense.

MISDREAVUS
TYPE:	Ghost
HEIGHT:	0.7m
WEIGHT:	1.0kg

Misdreavus likes to scare people by making a dreadful wailing sound. The red spheres around its neck seem to soak up the fear so the Pokémon can use it for food.

LEGENDARY

MOLTRES
TYPE:	Fire - Flying
HEIGHT:	2.0m
WEIGHT:	60.0kg

When Moltres gets hurt, some say it dives into an active volcano and heals itself by bathing in lava. This Legendary Pokémon can give off flames and control fire.

MISMAGIUS
TYPE:	Ghost
HEIGHT:	0.9m
WEIGHT:	4.4kg

Mismagius shows up unexpectedly, muttering in its chanting voice. Its chants often bring torment to those who listen.

MONFERNO
TYPE:	Fire - Fighting
HEIGHT:	0.9m
WEIGHT:	22.0kg

An excellent climber, Monferno can strike from above. It can flare up its tail flame to keep enemies at bay.

MOTHIM
TYPE:	Bug - Flying
HEIGHT:	0.9m
WEIGHT:	23.3kg

Mothim loves the taste of Combee's honey. Sometimes it will raid a hive at night to steal the sweet substance.

MR. MIME
TYPE:	Psychic - Fairy
HEIGHT:	1.3m
WEIGHT:	54.5kg

Sometimes, Mr. Mime's gestures convince an onlooker that the invisible thing it's miming actually exists. Then, that thing becomes real.

MUDKIP
TYPE:	Water
HEIGHT:	0.4m
WEIGHT:	7.6kg

Because its fin is so sensitive to the motion of air and water, Mudkip knows what's going on nearby without opening its eyes. The flared gills on its cheeks allow it to breathe underwater.

MUK
TYPE:	Poision
HEIGHT:	1.2m
WEIGHT:	30.0kg

Muk really stinks. The fluid it oozes gives off a terrible smell and pollutes clean water. Cities with a trash problem may also find they have a Muk problem.

MUNCHLAX
TYPE:	Normal
HEIGHT:	0.6m
WEIGHT:	105.0kg

Munchlax's long fur is a perfect place to hide snacks. With this permanent food stash, it never goes hungry.

MUNNA
TYPE:	Psychic
HEIGHT:	0.6m
WEIGHT:	23.3kg

When people and Pokémon sleep, Munna appears to eat their dreams and nightmares. After eating a happy dream, it gives off pink mist.

MURKROW
TYPE:	Dark - Flying
HEIGHT:	0.5m
WEIGHT:	2.1kg

People used to think Murkrow brought bad luck, so they were afraid of it and kept their distance. It's drawn to sparkly things and sometimes tries to steal them.

MUSHARNA
TYPE:	Psychic
HEIGHT:	1.1m
WEIGHT:	60.5kg

The dream mist that rises from Musharna's forehead is influenced by the dreams it eats. It can take on many different colors.

NATU
TYPE:	Psychic - Flying
HEIGHT:	0.2m
WEIGHT:	2.0kg

With its underdeveloped wings, Natu can't fly, but it's a great jumper, able to leap onto a tree branch higher than a grown man's head. It tends to engage in staring contests with those who meet its eyes.

NIDOKING
TYPE:	Poison - Ground
HEIGHT:	1.4m
WEIGHT:	62.0kg

When Nidoking swings its massive tail, it can knock down a radio tower. Nothing can stand in the way of its furious rampage.

NIDOQUEEN
TYPE:	Poison - Ground
HEIGHT:	1.3m
WEIGHT:	60.0kg

When defending its nest, Nidoqueen hurls its hard-scaled body at an intruder. The impact is often enough to send the enemy flying through the air.

NIDORAN ♀
TYPE:	Poison
HEIGHT:	0.4m
WEIGHT:	7.0kg

Though Nidoran ♀ is small, it's quite dangerous. The barbs in its fur and the horn on its head are both extremely poisonous.

NIDORAN ♂
TYPE:	Poison
HEIGHT:	0.5m
WEIGHT:	9.0kg

Nidoran ♂ has excellent hearing and, thanks to specialized muscles, it can move and rotate its ears to pick up the slightest sound.

NIDORINA
TYPE: Poison
HEIGHT: 0.8m
WEIGHT: 20.0kg

Nidorina are very social and become nervous on their own. When among friends, their poisonous barbs retract so they don't hurt anyone.

NIDORINO
TYPE: Poison
HEIGHT: 0.9m
WEIGHT: 19.5kg

The horn on Nidorino's forehead is made of an extremely hard substance. When challenged, its body bristles with poisonous barbs.

NINCADA
TYPE: Bug - Ground
HEIGHT: 0.5m
WEIGHT: 5.5kg

Nincada prefers to stay out of the sun, living underground and feeding on tree roots. When Evolution approaches, it stops moving altogether.

NINETALES
TYPE: Fire
HEIGHT: 1.1m
WEIGHT: 19.9kg

Ninetales can control an opponent's mind with the light from its red eyes. Stories say this Pokémon was formed when nine wizards merged into a single being.

NINJASK
TYPE: Bug - Flying
HEIGHT: 0.8m
WEIGHT: 12.0kg

Ninjask moves so fast that it's hard to see, although its cry is quite audible. Proper training is a must to keep its defiant nature in check.

NOCTOWL
TYPE: Normal - Flying
HEIGHT: 1.6m
WEIGHT: 40.8kg

With its excellent night vision and its silent wings, Noctowl is an expert when it comes to hunting in the darkness.

NOIBAT
TYPE: Flying - Dragon
HEIGHT: 0.5m
WEIGHT: 8.0kg

Noibat live in lightless caves and communicate with ultrasonic waves emitted from their ears. These waves can make a strong man dizzy.

NOIVERN
TYPE: Flying - Dragon
HEIGHT: 1.5m
WEIGHT: 85.0kg

Noivern are masters when it comes to battling in the dark. The ultrasonic waves they release from their ears are powerful enough to crush a boulder.

NOSEPASS
TYPE: Rock
HEIGHT: 1.0m
WEIGHT: 97.0kg

It's impossible for two Nosepass to stand face to face, because their magnetic noses repel each other. They move at a glacial pace.

NUMEL
TYPE: Fire - Ground
HEIGHT: 0.7m
WEIGHT: 24.0kg

The rather dull Numel sometimes doesn't notice when it's being attacked. Its body is full of magma, so Numel takes care to stay dry. Rain can make the magma cool and harden.

NUZLEAF
TYPE: Grass - Dark
HEIGHT: 1.0m
WEIGHT: 28.0kg

Nuzleaf can play the leaf on its head like a flute, and the music makes listeners nervous. It lives in dense forests and doesn't like visitors.

OCTILLERY
TYPE: Water
HEIGHT: 0.9m
WEIGHT: 28.5kg

In battle, Octillery wraps its opponent up in its tentacles to keep it from moving. If that doesn't work, it sprays a cloud of ink to cover its escape.

ODDISH
TYPE: Grass - Poison
HEIGHT: 0.5m
WEIGHT: 5.4kg

Oddish seeks out fertile ground where it can absorb nutrients from the soil. When it finds the perfect spot, it buries itself, and its feet apparently become like tree roots.

OMANYTE
TYPE: Rock - Water
HEIGHT: 0.4m
WEIGHT: 7.5kg

Omanyte's sturdy shell protects it from enemy attacks. This ancient Pokémon was restored from a fossil.

OMASTAR
TYPE: Rock - Water
HEIGHT: 1.0m
WEIGHT: 35.0kg

Some suspect that Omastar went extinct because it could no longer carry its heavy shell with ease. It seeks out food with its tentacles.

ONIX
TYPE: Rock - Ground
HEIGHT: 8.8m
WEIGHT: 210.0kg

Thanks to its internal magnet, Onix never loses its way while boring through the ground. Its body grows smoother with age as the rough edges wear away.

OSHAWOTT
TYPE: Water
HEIGHT: 0.5m
WEIGHT: 5.9kg

Oshawott can detach the scalchop on its belly and use it as a weapon in battle or as a tool for cutting up food and other things.

PACHIRISU
TYPE: Electric
HEIGHT: 0.4m
WEIGHT: 3.9kg

When Pachirisu affectionately rub their cheeks together, they're sharing electric energy with each other. The balls of fur they shed crackle with static.

LEGENDARY

PALKIA
TYPE: Water - Dragon
HEIGHT: 4.2m
WEIGHT: 336.0kg

It is said Palkia can cause rents and distortions in space. In ancient times, it was revered as a legend.

PALPITOAD
TYPE: Water - Ground
HEIGHT: 0.8m
WEIGHT: 17.0kg

With the vibrations of its head bumps, Palpitoad can make ripples in the water or cause seismic activity. Its long tongue is coated in a sticky substance.

PANCHAM
TYPE: Fighting
HEIGHT: 0.6m
WEIGHT: 8.0kg

Pancham tries to be intimidating, but it's just too cute. When someone pats it on the head, it drops the tough-guy act and grins.

PANGORO
TYPE: Fighting - Dark
HEIGHT: 2.1m
WEIGHT: 136.0kg

The leafy sprig Pangoro holds in its mouth helps the Pokémon track its opponents' movements. Taking hits in battle doesn't seem to bother it at all.

PANPOUR
TYPE: Water
HEIGHT: 0.6m
WEIGHT: 13.5kg

Panpour's head tuft is full of nutrient-rich water. It uses its tail to water plants, which then grow big and healthy.

PANSAGE
TYPE: Grass
HEIGHT: 0.6m
WEIGHT: 10.5kg

Chewing the leaf from Pansage's head is a known method of stress relief. It willingly shares its leaf–along with any berries it's collected–with those who need it.

PANSEAR
TYPE: Fire
HEIGHT: 0.6m
WEIGHT: 11.0kg

Clever and helpful, Pansear prefers to cook its berries rather than eating them raw. Its natural habitat is volcanic caves, so it's no surprise that its fiery tuft burns at 600 degrees Fahrenheit.

PARAS
TYPE: Bug - Grass
HEIGHT: 0.3m
WEIGHT: 5.4kg

Mushrooms called tochukaso grow on Paras's back. Some people use them in medicines.

PARASECT
TYPE: Bug - Grass
HEIGHT: 1.0m
WEIGHT: 29.5kg

Parasect feed on the roots of trees. If a group of them infests the same tree, they can be very destructive.

PATRAT
TYPE: Normal
HEIGHT: 0.5m
WEIGHT: 11.6kg

Wary and cautious, Patrat are very serious about their job as lookouts. They store food in their cheeks so they don't have to leave their post.

PAWNIARD
TYPE: Dark - Steel
HEIGHT: 0.5m
WEIGHT: 10.2kg

Pawniard's body is covered in blades, which it keeps sharp by polishing them after battle. Even when hurt, it's a relentless hunter.

PELIPPER
TYPE: Water - Flying
HEIGHT: 1.2m
WEIGHT: 28.0kg

Flying low over the waves, Pelipper catches food by dipping its huge bill into the water. Its bill is big enough that it can even carry small Pokémon from place to place.

PERSIAN
TYPE: Normal
HEIGHT: 1.0m
WEIGHT: 32.0kg

Persian uses its distinctive whiskers as sensors to find out about its surroundings. Grabbing the whiskers makes it meek and docile.

PETILIL
TYPE: Grass
HEIGHT: 0.5m
WEIGHT: 6.6kg

When many Petilil settle in an area, gardeners and farmers pay attention, because these Pokémon seek out rich soil that's good for growing plants. Their leaves have healing properties.

PHANPY
TYPE: Ground
HEIGHT: 0.5m
WEIGHT: 33.5kg

Phanpy sucks up water with its long trunk to spray itself for a bath, or to playfully squirt others. It makes its nest by digging into a riverbank.

PHANTUMP
TYPE: Ghost - Grass
HEIGHT: 0.4m
WEIGHT: 7.0kg

It is said that when the spirits of wandering children inhabit old tree stumps, these Pokémon are created. Phantump dwell in lonely forests, far away from people.

MYTHICAL

PHIONE
TYPE: Water
HEIGHT: 0.4m
WEIGHT: 3.1kg

Phione gather in large groups as they drift with the current through warm seas. After floating for a time, they always return home, no matter how far they have traveled.

PICHU
TYPE: Electric
HEIGHT: 0.3m
WEIGHT: 2.0kg

Sometimes, when two Pichu play together, the static electricity that crackles off their bodies produces an unexpected shower of sparks. This often startles them into crying.

PIDGEOT
TYPE: Normal - Flying
HEIGHT: 1.5m
WEIGHT: 39.5kg

Many Trainers are drawn to Pidgeot because of its lovely feathers. The beautiful colors of its crest are particularly striking.

PIDGEOTTO
TYPE: Normal - Flying
HEIGHT: 1.1m
WEIGHT: 30.0kg

Very territorial, Pidgeotto keeps up a steady patrol of the large area it claims as its own. Any intruder will be driven off with merciless attacks from its sharp claws.

PIDGEY
TYPE: Normal - Flying
HEIGHT: 0.3m
WEIGHT: 1.8kg

Thanks to Pidgey's excellent sense of direction, it can always find its way home, no matter how far it has traveled.

PIDOVE
TYPE: Normal - Flying
HEIGHT: 0.3m
WEIGHT: 2.1kg

Even wild Pidove are used to having people around. They live in cities and often flock to places where people spend time, like plazas and parks.

PIKACHU
TYPE: Electric
HEIGHT: 0.4m
WEIGHT: 6.0kg

The red pouches on Pikachu's cheeks store up electricity while it sleeps. It often delivers a zap when encountering something unfamiliar.

PIGNITE
TYPE: Fire - Fighting
HEIGHT: 1.0m
WEIGHT: 55.5kg

"Food is fuel"—for Pignite, that common phrase is a bit more literal. When it eats, its internal fire is stoked, which increases its power and speed.

PILOSWINE
TYPE: Ice - Ground
HEIGHT: 1.1m
WEIGHT: 55.8kg

Piloswine's long, thick hair helps protect it from the intense cold of its surroundings. Its tusks can dig through the ice to find buried food.

PINECO
TYPE: Bug
HEIGHT: 0.6m
WEIGHT: 7.2kg

Don't disturb Pineco while it's eating! Most of the time it patiently hangs onto a branch, but if it's dislodged during a meal, it will fall to the ground and explode.

PINSIR
TYPE: Bug
HEIGHT: 1.5m
WEIGHT: 55.0kg

When its strong pincer gets a grip, Pinsir can lift an enemy much bigger than itself. The thorns that line its horns dig into its opponent, making it hard to get away.

PIPLUP
TYPE: Water
HEIGHT: 0.4m
WEIGHT: 5.2kg

Proud and stubborn, Piplup can be a challenge to train. It's quite independent, preferring to take care of itself and find its own food.

PLUSLE
TYPE: Electric
HEIGHT: 0.4m
WEIGHT: 4.2kg

Plusle can short out the electricity in its body to create a crackling shower of sparks! It always cheers on its friends in battle.

POLITOED
TYPE: Water
HEIGHT: 1.1m
WEIGHT: 33.9kg

Politoed has a single long, curly hair on the top of its head, which marks it as a ruler. Apparently, a longer hair with more curl is more respected by others.

POLIWAG
TYPE: Water
HEIGHT: 0.6m
WEIGHT: 12.4kg

Poliwag's skin is so thin that you can see right through it to the Pokémon's spiral-shaped insides. Fortunately, it's also very resilient and flexible.

POLIWHIRL
TYPE: Water
HEIGHT: 1.0m
WEIGHT: 20.0kg

Poliwhirl is covered with a slick, slippery, slimy fluid that allows it to wriggle out of sticky situations.

POLIWRATH
TYPE: Water - Fighting
HEIGHT: 1.3m
WEIGHT: 54.0kg

Burly and muscular, Poliwrath can exercise for hours without getting tired. It swims effortlessly through the ocean.

PONYTA
TYPE: Fire
HEIGHT: 1.0m
WEIGHT: 30.0kg

At the beginning of its life, Ponyta's legs are too weak to hold it up. It quickly learns to run by chasing after its elders.

POOCHYENA
TYPE: Dark
HEIGHT: 0.5m
WEIGHT: 13.6kg

Poochyena tries to look bigger than it is by bristling up its tail. It tends to react to unexpected movement by biting, and it easily chases prey to exhaustion.

PORYGON
TYPE: Normal
HEIGHT: 0.8m
WEIGHT: 36.5kg

Porygon was created from programming code, and it can return to that form to navigate cyberspace. It can't be copied like regular data.

PORYGON2
TYPE: Normal
HEIGHT: 0.6m
WEIGHT: 32.5kg

Porygon2 is the product of human ingenuity. Programmed with artificial intelligence, it is capable of learning new things.

PORYGON-Z
TYPE: Normal
HEIGHT: 0.9m
WEIGHT: 34.0kg

Changes in its programming were intended to allow Porygon-Z to travel to other dimensions, but something went awry during the upgrade, and it began behaving erratically.

PRIMAL GROUDON
TYPE: Ground - Fire
HEIGHT: 5.0m
WEIGHT: 999.7kg

PRIMAL KYOGRE
TYPE: Water
HEIGHT: 9.8m
WEIGHT: 430.0kg

PRIMEAPE
TYPE: Fighting
HEIGHT: 1.0m
WEIGHT: 32.0kg

Fury increases Primeape's blood flow and powers up its muscles. Its intelligence drops sharply during a rage.

PRINPLUP
TYPE: Water
HEIGHT: 0.8m
WEIGHT: 23.0kg

Because Prinplup have a strong sense of self-importance, they tend to live alone. They can topple trees by striking with their wings.

PROBOPASS
TYPE: Rock - Steel
HEIGHT: 1.4m
WEIGHT: 340.0kg

Probopass uses the strong magnetic field it generates to control the three smaller Mini-Noses attached to the sides of its body.

PSYDUCK
TYPE: Water
HEIGHT: 0.8m
WEIGHT: 19.6kg

Though Psyduck can use mysterious psychic powers, it can never remember doing so. Apparently, this power creates strange brain waves that resemble deep slumber.

PUMPKABOO
TYPE: Ghost - Grass
HEIGHT: 10.4m
WEIGHT: 50.0kg

The nocturnal Pumpkaboo tends to get restless as darkness falls. Stories say it serves as a guide for wandering spirits, leading them through the night to find their true home.

PUPITAR
TYPE: Rock - Ground
HEIGHT: 1.2m
WEIGHT: 152.0kg

Pupitar moves by propulsion, expelling compressed gases to launch itself forward. Its hard surface protects it when it hits solid objects.

PURRLOIN
TYPE: Dark
HEIGHT: 0.4m
WEIGHT: 10.1kg

Purrloin acts cute and innocent to trick people into trusting it. Then it steals their stuff.

PURUGLY
TYPE: Normal
HEIGHT: 1.0m
WEIGHT: 43.8kg

Purugly wraps its two tails around its waist to make itself look bigger. It's been known to kick other Pokémon out of their comfortable nests and take over.

PYROAR
TYPE: Fire - Normal
HEIGHT: 1.5m
WEIGHT: 81.5kg

Pyroar live together in prides, led by the male whose fiery mane is the biggest. The females of the pride guard the young.

QUAGSIRE
TYPE: Water - Ground
HEIGHT: 1.4m
WEIGHT: 75.0kg

Quagsire doesn't exactly hunt for food—it hangs out in the water with its mouth open and waits for something to drift in. Fortunately, this lack of movement means it doesn't need to eat much.

QUILAVA
TYPE: Fire
HEIGHT: 0.9m
WEIGHT: 19.0kg

To keep opponents from getting too close, Quilava heats up the air around it by flaring the flames on its body. It's extremely nimble and good at dodging.

QUILLADIN
TYPE: Grass
HEIGHT: 0.7m
WEIGHT: 29.0kg

Quilladin often train for battle by charging forcefully into each other. Despite their spiky appearance, they have a gentle nature and don't like confrontation.

QWILFISH
TYPE: Water - Poison
HEIGHT: 0.5m
WEIGHT: 3.9kg

Qwilfish puffs up its body by sucking in water, then uses that water pressure to send the poisonous spikes that cover it shooting outward at an opponent.

RAICHU
TYPE: Electric
HEIGHT: 0.8m
WEIGHT: 30.0kg

When overcharged with electricity, Raichu sinks its tail into the ground to get rid of the excess. The charge makes it glow faintly in the dark.

LEGENDARY

RAIKOU

TYPE: Electric
HEIGHT: 1.9m
WEIGHT: 178.0kg

When Raikou roars, the air and land shudder. This Legendary Pokémon moves with lightning speed.

RALTS

TYPE: Psychic - Fairy
HEIGHT: 0.4m
WEIGHT: 6.6kg

With its horns, Ralts can sense people's emotions. Its own mood tends to reflect what it senses, and it's drawn to people with a positive attitude.

RAMPARDOS

TYPE: Rock
HEIGHT: 1.6m
WEIGHT: 102.5kg

Rampardos can smash through anything with its skull, which is iron-hard and incredibly thick. Unfortunately, this means its brain has no room to grow.

RAPIDASH

TYPE: Fire
HEIGHT: 1.7m
WEIGHT: 95.0kg

Most of the time, Rapidash travels at a casual canter across the flat lands where it lives. When it breaks into a gallop, its mane blazes brightly.

RATICATE

TYPE: Normal
HEIGHT: 0.7m
WEIGHT: 18.5kg

Because Raticate's fangs never stop growing, it has to gnaw on hard objects to whittle them down. Logs and rocks often serve this purpose, but sometimes it chews on houses!

RATTATA

TYPE: Normal
HEIGHT: 0.3m
WEIGHT: 3.5kg

Rattata is always on the alert, keeping an ear out for the slightest sound even in its sleep. It's happy to nest just about anywhere.

RELICANTH

TYPE: Water - Rock
HEIGHT: 1.0m
WEIGHT: 23.4kg

Relicanth today look much the same as they did 100 million years ago. These ancient Pokémon are covered in rocky scales to protect them in the ocean depths.

LEGENDARY

RAYQUAZA

TYPE: Dragon - Flying
HEIGHT: 7.0m
WEIGHT: 206.5kg

Legends say the ancient Pokémon Rayquaza flies through the upper atmosphere and feeds on meteoroids. It's known for stopping the endless battles between Kyogre and Groudon.

REMORAID

TYPE: Water
HEIGHT: 0.6m
WEIGHT: 12.0kg

Remoraid can knock flying targets out of the air with precise jets of high-velocity water. It swims downstream when it's time to evolve.

LEGENDARY

REGICE

TYPE: Ice
HEIGHT: 1.8m
WEIGHT: 175.0kg

Created during an ice age, Regice's body is frozen solid, and even lava can't melt it. It can lower the temperature of the air around it by several hundred degrees.

LEGENDARY

REGIGIGAS

TYPE: Normal
HEIGHT: 3.7m
WEIGHT: 420.0kg

According to legend, Regigigas built smaller models of itself out of rock, ice, and magma. It's so enormous that it could tow an entire continent behind it.

LEGENDARY

REGIROCK

TYPE: Rock
HEIGHT: 1.7m
WEIGHT: 230.0kg

Regirock's body is made entirely of rocks, and these rocks were recently discovered to be from all around the world. It repairs itself after battle by seeking out new rocks.

LEGENDARY

REGISTEEL

TYPE: Steel
HEIGHT: 1.9m
WEIGHT: 205.0kg

Registeel isn't actually made of steel—it's a strange substance harder than any known metal. Ancient people sealed it away in a prison.

REUNICLUS

TYPE: Psychic
HEIGHT: 1.0m
WEIGHT: 20.1kg

Reuniclus shake hands with each other to create a network between their brains. Working together boosts their psychic power, and they can crush huge rocks with their minds.

LEGENDARY

RESHIRAM
TYPE: Dragon - Fire
HEIGHT: 3.2m
WEIGHT: 330.0kg

Legends say Reshiram is drawn to those who value the truth. The flare of its fiery tail can disrupt the atmosphere and cause strange weather patterns.

RHYDON
TYPE: Ground - Rock
HEIGHT: 1.9m
WEIGHT: 120.0kg

Rhydon's horn, which it uses as a drill, is hard enough to crush diamonds. Its hide is like armor, and it can run right through molten lava without feeling a thing.

RHYHORN
TYPE: Ground - Rock
HEIGHT: 1.0m
WEIGHT: 115.0kg

A charging Rhyhorn is so single-minded that it doesn't think about anything else until it demolishes its target.

RHYPERIOR
TYPE: Ground - Rock
HEIGHT: 2.4m
WEIGHT: 282.8kg

Rhyperior uses the holes in its hands to bombard its opponents with rocks. Sometimes it even hurls a Geodude! Rhyperior's rocky hide is thick enough to protect it from molten lava.

RIOLU
TYPE: Fighting
HEIGHT: 0.7m
WEIGHT: 20.2g

The aura surrounding Riolu's body indicates its emotional state. It alters the shape of this aura to communicate.

ROGGENROLA
TYPE: Rock
HEIGHT: 0.4m
WEIGHT: 18.0kg

Each Roggenrola has an energy core at its center. The intense pressure in their underground home has compressed their bodies into a steely toughness.

ROSELIA
TYPE: Grass - Poison
HEIGHT: 0.3m
WEIGHT: 2.0kg

Thieves sometimes try to swipe the lovely blossoms Roselia grows. It responds with a shower of sharp, poisonous thorns.

ROSERADE
TYPE: Grass - Poison
HEIGHT: 0.9m
WEIGHT: 14.5kg

With its beautiful blooms, enticing aroma, and graceful movements, Roserade is quite enchanting—but watch out! Its arms conceal thorny whips, and the thorns carry poison.

ROTOM
TYPE: Electric - Ghost
HEIGHT: 0.3m
WEIGHT: 0.3kg

Scientists are conducting ongoing research on Rotom, which shows potential as a power source. Sometimes, it sneaks into electrical appliances and causes trouble.

RUFFLET
TYPE: Normal - Flying
HEIGHT: 0.5m
WEIGHT: 10.5kg

Rufflet is absolutely fearless when challenging opponents. It will pick a fight with just about anyone, becoming stronger in the process.

SABLEYE
TYPE: Dark - Ghost
HEIGHT: 0.5m
WEIGHT: 11.0kg

Sableye lives deep in a cave, where it uses its sharp claws to dig up rocks for food. Minerals from these rocks then become part of its gemstone eyes and the crystals on its body.

SALAMENCE
TYPE: Dragon - Flying
HEIGHT: 1.5m
WEIGHT: 102.6kg

When it evolves, Salamence finally grows the wings it's always dreamed of. It trails fire across the sky in a soaring celebration.

SAMUROTT
TYPE: Water
HEIGHT: 1.5m
WEIGHT: 94.6kg

From the armor on its front legs, Samurott can draw its swordlike seamitars in a heartbeat. Its glare can make everyone behave.

SANDILE
TYPE: Ground - Dark
HEIGHT: 0.7m
WEIGHT: 15.2kg

Sandile travels just below the surface of the desert sand, with only its nose and eyes sticking out. The warmth of the sand keeps it from getting too cold.

SANDSHREW
TYPE: Ground
HEIGHT: 0.6m
WEIGHT: 12.0kg

When Sandshrew rolls up into a ball, its tough hide helps keep it safe. It lives in the desert and sleeps in a burrow under the sand.

SANDSLASH
TYPE: Ground
HEIGHT: 1.0m
WEIGHT: 29.5kg

Sections of hardened hide form the spikes that cover Sandslash's body. The spikes protect it in battle and can also be used as a weapon.

SAWK
TYPE: Fighting
HEIGHT: 1.4m
WEIGHT: 51.0kg

Sawk go deep into the mountains to train their fighting skills relentlessly. If they are disturbed during this training, they become very angry.

SAWSBUCK
TYPE: Normal - Grass
HEIGHT: 1.9m
WEIGHT: 92.5kg

As the seasons change, their horns display different kinds of plant growth. Because of their seasonal migration, some people regard Sawsbuck's appearance as a sign of spring.

SCATTERBUG
TYPE: Bug
HEIGHT: 0.3m
WEIGHT: 2.5kg

When threatened, Scatterbug protects itself with a cloud of black powder that can paralyze its attacker. This powder also serves as protection from the elements.

SCEPTILE
TYPE: Grass
HEIGHT: 1.5m
WEIGHT: 52.5kg

Razor-edged leaves and nutritious seeds sprout from Sceptile's back. It wields the leaves in battle, and cares for trees by planting its seeds nearby to enrich the soil.

SCIZOR
TYPE: Bug - Steel
HEIGHT: 1.8m
WEIGHT: 118.0kg

Scizor's exoskeleton is as hard as steel, easily shrugging off most ordinary attacks. It controls its internal temperature by flapping its wings.

SCOLIPEDE
TYPE: Bug - Poison
HEIGHT: 2.5m
WEIGHT: 200.5kg

The claws near Scolipede's head can be used to grab, immobilize, and poison its opponent. It moves quickly when chasing down enemies.

SCRAFTY
TYPE: Dark - Fighting
HEIGHT: 1.1m
WEIGHT: 30.0kg

A group of Scrafty is led by the one with the biggest crest. Their powerful kicks can shatter concrete.

SCRAGGY
TYPE: Dark - Fighting
HEIGHT: 0.6m
WEIGHT: 11.8kg

Scraggy can pull its loose, rubbery skin up around its neck to protect itself from attacks. With its tough skull, it delivers headbutts without warning.

SCYTHER
TYPE: Bug - Flying
HEIGHT: 1.5m
WEIGHT: 56.0kg

With its impressive speed and razor-sharp scythes, Scyther is a formidable opponent. It can slash through a log with one blow.

SEADRA
TYPE: Water
HEIGHT: 1.2m
WEIGHT: 25.0kg

When Seadra spins around in the water, it can cause a whirlpool with enough force to capsize a small boat. It sleeps among coral branches.

SEAKING
TYPE: Water
HEIGHT: 1.3m
WEIGHT: 39.0kg

Male Seaking become brilliantly colored during the autumn, when they perform their courtship dance. The pair take turns keeping watch over their nests.

SEALEO
TYPE: Ice - Water
HEIGHT: 1.1m
WEIGHT: 87.6kg

Sealeo learns about new things by exploring them with its nose, examining the fragrance and texture. It particularly enjoys spinning round objects on its nose.

SEEDOT
TYPE: Grass
HEIGHT: 0.5m
WEIGHT: 4.0kg

Because Seedot hangs from branches by the top of its head, it looks just like an acorn when it isn't moving. For a glossy finish, it drinks plenty of water and polishes itself with leaves.

SEEL
TYPE: Water
HEIGHT: 1.1m
WEIGHT: 90.0kg

In frozen seas, Seel swims under the ice in search of food. It uses the point on its head to break through the ice when it comes up for air.

SEISMITOAD
TYPE: Water - Ground
HEIGHT: 1.5m
WEIGHT: 62.0kg

When Seismitoad vibrates the bumps on its hands, its punches get a serious power boost—enough to pulverize a boulder with a single hit.

SENTRET
TYPE: Normal
HEIGHT: 0.8m
WEIGHT: 6.0kg

Sentret always sleep in groups of two or more so one of them can keep watch and alert its friends if danger threatens. When alone, they're too nervous to sleep.

SERPERIOR
TYPE: Grass
HEIGHT: 3.3m
WEIGHT: 63.0kg

A single glare from Serperior can stop most opponents in their tracks. The energy it absorbs from the sun gets a boost inside its body.

SERVINE
TYPE: Grass
HEIGHT: 0.8m
WEIGHT: 16.0kg

Dirt on its leaves blocks its photosynthesis, so Servine is fussy about staying clean. It confounds its enemies with quick movements before it strikes with its whiplike vines.

SEWADDLE
TYPE: Bug - Grass
HEIGHT: 0.3m
WEIGHT: 25.0kg

Sewaddle makes clothing for itself by sewing leaves together with the sticky thread it produces from its mouth. Fashion designers often use it as a mascot.

SHARPEDO
TYPE: Water - Dark
HEIGHT: 1.8m
WEIGHT: 88.8kg

Though Sharpedo isn't great at swimming long distances, it can shoot forward at 75 mph by propelling seawater through its body. If a tooth falls out, it grows back immediately.

SEVIPER
TYPE: Poison
HEIGHT: 2.7m
WEIGHT: 52.5kg

The sharp blade on Seviper's tail also gives off a powerful poison. These Pokémon constantly feud with Zangoose.

MYTHICAL

SHAYMIN
TYPE: Grass	
HEIGHT: 0.2m	When the Gracidea flower blooms, Shaymin gains the power of flight. Wherever it goes, it clears the air of toxins and brings feelings of gratitude.
WEIGHT: 2.1kg	

SHEDINJA
TYPE: Bug - Ghost
HEIGHT: 0.8m
WEIGHT: 1.2kg

Shedinja is a strange Pokémon. It doesn't move, it doesn't breathe, and no one really knows where it came from. Its body seems to be nothing more than a hollow shell.

SHELGON
TYPE: Dragon
HEIGHT: 1.1m
WEIGHT: 110.5kg

A shell of thick armor protects Shelgon while it prepares to evolve. It's hard enough to repel enemy attacks, and so heavy that it makes the Pokémon move slowly.

SHELLDER
TYPE: Water
HEIGHT: 0.3m
WEIGHT: 4.0kg

When Shellder's shell is closed, its large tongue tends to hang out. It uses its tongue as a shovel to dig a nest in the sand.

SHELLOS
TYPE: Water
HEIGHT: 0.3m
WEIGHT: 6.3kg

Shellos come in different colors and shapes, depending on where they live. Their squishy bodies give off a strange purple fluid when pressure is applied.

SHELMET
TYPE: Bug
HEIGHT: 0.4m
WEIGHT: 7.7kg

Shelmet evolves when exposed to electricity, but only if Karrablast is nearby. It's unclear why this is the case.

SHIELDON
TYPE: Rock - Steel
HEIGHT: 0.5m
WEIGHT: 57.0kg

Though Shieldon's face is well protected by its polished armor, it's vulnerable if a foe strikes from behind. It was restored from a fossil.

SHIFTRY
TYPE: Grass - Dark
HEIGHT: 1.3m
WEIGHT: 59.6kg

Shiftry makes its home in the tops of ancient trees. Its leafy fans can stir up powerful gusts of wind.

SHINX
TYPE: Electric
HEIGHT: 0.5m
WEIGHT: 9.5kg

When Shinx senses danger, its fur gives off a bright flash. This brilliant light blinds its attacker so Shinx can make a hasty escape.

SHROOMISH
TYPE: Grass
HEIGHT: 0.4m
WEIGHT: 4.5kg

Shroomish live deep in the forest and make their home in moist soil, using rotted plant material as food. The spores it shakes from its cap are poisonous.

SHUCKLE
TYPE: Bug - Rock
HEIGHT: 0.6m
WEIGHT: 20.5kg

Shuckle stores berries in its shell so it always has a food supply. This comes in handy when it hides away under the rocks.

SHUPPET
TYPE: Ghost
HEIGHT: 0.6m
WEIGHT: 2.3kg

If someone is consumed by thoughts of revenge, it's likely a Shuppet is lurking nearby, drawing energy from those dark feelings.

SIGILYPH
TYPE: Psychic - Flying
HEIGHT: 1.4m
WEIGHT: 14.0kg

Sigilyph were appointed to keep watch over an ancient city. Their patrol route never varies.

SILCOON
TYPE: Bug
HEIGHT: 0.6m
WEIGHT: 10.0kg

While waiting to evolve, Silcoon wraps its body in silk and attaches itself to a branch. It leaves a tiny hole so it can see. The cocoon protects the Pokémon and collects rainwater so it can drink.

SIMIPOUR
TYPE: Water
HEIGHT: 1.0m
WEIGHT: 29.0kg

Simipour can shoot water out of its tail with such force that it can punch right through a concrete wall. When its stores run low, it dips its tail into clean water to suck up a refill.

SIMISAGE
TYPE: Grass
HEIGHT: 1.1m
WEIGHT: 30.5kg

Simisage's tail is covered in thorns, and it uses the tail like a whip to lash out at opponents. It always seems to be in a bad mood.

SIMISEAR
TYPE: Fire
HEIGHT: 1.0m
WEIGHT: 28.0kg

Simisear's head and tail give off embers in the heat of battle...or anytime it's excited. It has quite a sweet tooth.

SKARMORY
TYPE: Steel - Flying	
HEIGHT: 1.7m	The steel that makes up Skarmory's wings gets dinged up and dented during battles. Every year, the sharp edges renew themselves.
WEIGHT: 50.0kg	

SKIDDO
TYPE: Grass
HEIGHT: 0.9m
WEIGHT: 31.0kg

Calm and gentle, Skiddo have been living side by side with people for many generations. They can create energy via photosynthesis.

SKIPLOOM
TYPE: Grass - Flying
HEIGHT: 0.6m
WEIGHT: 1.0kg

In mild temperatures, the flower on Skiploom's head begins to bloom. The petals start to open at just above 64 degrees Fahrenheit, and warmer temperatures coax them into full blossom.

SKITTY
TYPE: Normal
HEIGHT: 0.6m
WEIGHT: 11.0kg

Anything that moves, including its own tail, draws Skitty's attention and starts a playful game of chase. Wild Skitty live in trees.

SKORUPI
TYPE: Poison - Bug
HEIGHT: 0.8m
WEIGHT: 12.0kg

After burying itself in the sand, Skorupi lurks in hiding. If an intruder gets too close, it latches on with the poisonous claws on its tail.

SKRELP
TYPE: Poison - Water
HEIGHT: 0.5m
WEIGHT: 7.3kg

Skrelp disguises itself as rotten kelp to hide from enemies. It defends itself by spraying a poisonous liquid.

SKUNTANK
TYPE: Poison - Dark
HEIGHT: 1.0m
WEIGHT: 38.0kg

From the end of its tail, Skuntank can shoot a noxious fluid more than 160 feet. This fluid smells awful, and the stench only gets worse if it's not cleaned up immediately.

SLAKING
TYPE: Normal
HEIGHT: 2.0m
WEIGHT: 130.5kg

Slaking lies in one place and pulls up grass to eat. Circular bare spots in a meadow might be a sign that a Slaking lives nearby. After eating everything within reach, it moves to another spot, but it's not happy about that.

SLAKOTH
TYPE: Normal
HEIGHT: 0.8m
WEIGHT: 24.0kg

It's rare to see a Slakoth move. It's awake for only a few hours per day, its heart beats extremely slowly, and it doesn't require much food.

SLIGGOO
TYPE: Dragon
HEIGHT: 0.8m
WEIGHT: 17.5kg

The four horns on Sliggoo's head are sense organs that allow the Pokémon to find its way by sound and smell.

SLOWBRO
TYPE: Water - Psychic
HEIGHT: 1.6m
WEIGHT: 78.5kg

Because of the Shellder chomping on its tail, Slowbro can no longer spend its days fishing. It can swim to catch food, but it's not happy about that.

SLOWKING
TYPE: Water - Psychic
HEIGHT: 2.0m
WEIGHT: 79.5kg

If the Shellder on its head were to let go, Slowking would forget all its knowledge. It spends time in research every day, trying to solve the world's greatest mysteries.

SLOWPOKE
TYPE: Water - Psychic
HEIGHT: 1.2m
WEIGHT: 36.0kg

Slowpoke spends much of its time along the riverbank, where it uses its tail for fishing. Often, its mind wanders and it spends the whole day lazing about.

SLUGMA
TYPE: Fire
HEIGHT: 0.7m
WEIGHT: 35.0kg

The magma that circulates within Slugma's body serves as its blood, supplying its organs with oxygen and nutrients. It has to stay warm, or the magma will harden.

SLURPUFF
TYPE: Fairy
HEIGHT: 0.8m
WEIGHT: 5.0kg

Pastry chefs love having a Slurpuff in the kitchen. With its incredibly sensitive nose, it can tell exactly when a dessert is baked to perfection.

SMEARGLE
TYPE: Normal
HEIGHT: 1.2m
WEIGHT: 58.0kg

Smeargle's tail tip produces a fluid that it uses like paint to draw thousands of different territorial markings.

SMOOCHUM
TYPE: Ice - Psychic
HEIGHT: 0.4m
WEIGHT: 6.0kg

Very active but a little clumsy, Smoochum falls down a lot when it runs. After falling, it seeks out a reflective surface so it can make sure its face isn't smudged.

SNEASEL
TYPE: Dark - Ice
HEIGHT: 0.9m
WEIGHT: 28.0kg

When Sneasel climbs trees, its hook-like claws sink into the bark to give it a good grip. It sometimes raids unprotected nests for food.

SNIVY
TYPE: Grass
HEIGHT: 0.6m
WEIGHT: 8.1kg

Soaking up sunlight with its tail increases Snivy's speed. Though it has hands, it generally uses the vines that extend from its neck instead.

SNORLAX
TYPE: Normal
HEIGHT: 2.1m
WEIGHT: 460.0kg

Snorlax spends most of its time eating and sleeping. Small children sometimes play by bouncing on this gentle Pokémon's vast belly.

SNORUNT
TYPE: Ice
HEIGHT: 0.7m
WEIGHT: 16.8kg

They say that when a Snorunt visits your home, it brings good fortune that will last. It eats snow and spends the warmer seasons hidden deep in caves.

SNOVER
TYPE: Grass - Ice
HEIGHT: 1.0m
WEIGHT: 50.5kg

Snover live high in the mountains most of the year, but in the winter, they migrate to lower elevations.

SNUBBULL
TYPE: Fairy
HEIGHT: 0.6m
WEIGHT: 7.8kg

Snubbull can drive off smaller Pokémon by making scary faces at them. After they run away, it seems to regret its behavior.

SOLOSIS
TYPE: Psychic
HEIGHT: 0.3m
WEIGHT: 1.0kg

The special liquid that surrounds Solosis protects it from any harsh conditions. They communicate with telepathy.

SOLROCK
TYPE: Rock - Psychic
HEIGHT: 1.2m
WEIGHT: 154.0kg

When Solrock spins, it gives off heat and light. It uses sunlight for energy and can apparently pick up on others' emotions.

SPEAROW
TYPE: Normal - Flying
HEIGHT: 0.3m
WEIGHT: 2.0kg

When many Spearow sound their loud, high-pitched cry all at once, it usually means danger is nearby.

SPEWPA
TYPE: Bug
HEIGHT: 0.3m
WEIGHT: 8.4kg

Like Scatterbug, Spewpa releases a protective cloud of powder when attacked. It can also bristle up its thick fur in an attempt to scare off any aggressors.

SPHEAL
TYPE: Ice - Water
HEIGHT: 0.8m
WEIGHT: 39.5kg

Spheal can roll across the ice faster than it can walk. When it's happy, it bursts into applause by clapping its fins together, so a group of joyful Spheal is rather noisy.

SPINARAK
TYPE: Bug - Poison
HEIGHT: 0.5m
WEIGHT: 8.5kg

Spinarak uses its web like another sensory organ. It can read the vibration of the strands to tell what's happening nearby.

SPINDA
TYPE: Normal
HEIGHT: 1.1m
WEIGHT: 5.0kg

It's said that no two Spinda have the same pattern of spots. They stumble and totter when they walk, making their opponents dizzy.

SPIRITOMB
TYPE: Ghost - Dark
HEIGHT: 1.0m
WEIGHT: 108.0kg

Long ago, Spiritomb was bound to an odd keystone as punishment for bad behavior. Its body is formed of more than a hundred spirits.

SPOINK
TYPE: Psychic
HEIGHT: 0.7m
WEIGHT: 30.6kg

The constant bouncing motion of Spoink's springy tail regulates its heartbeat. It's always looking for a bigger pearl for its head, because the jewel focuses its psychic powers.

SPRITZEE
TYPE: Fairy
HEIGHT: 0.2m
WEIGHT: 0.5kg

Long ago, this Pokémon was popular among the nobility for its lovely scent. Instead of spraying perfume, ladies would keep a Spritzee close at hand.

SQUIRTLE
TYPE: Water
HEIGHT: 0.5m
WEIGHT: 9.0kg

With its aerodynamic shape and grooved surface, Squirtle's shell helps it cut through the water very quickly. It also offers protection in battle.

STANTLER
TYPE: Normal
HEIGHT: 1.4m
WEIGHT: 71.2kg

The intricately curved antlers that grow from Stantler's head have been regarded as priceless works of art by collectors.

STARAPTOR
TYPE: Normal - Flying
HEIGHT: 1.2m
WEIGHT: 24.9kg

After evolving, Staraptor go off on their own, leaving their flocks behind. With their strong wings, they can fly with ease even when carrying a burden.

STARAVIA
TYPE: Normal - Flying
HEIGHT: 0.6m
WEIGHT: 15.5kg

Staravia travel in large flocks that can be very territorial. Battles sometimes break out between two competing flocks.

STARLY
TYPE: Normal - Flying
HEIGHT: 0.3m
WEIGHT: 2.0kg

Huge flocks of Starly gather in fields and mountains. In such large numbers, their wings flap with impressive power...and their noisy singing is quite a nuisance!

STARMIE
TYPE: Water - Psychic
HEIGHT: 1.1m
WEIGHT: 80.0kg

Because of the glowing rainbow of colors produced by Starmie's core, this Pokémon is known as "the gem of the sea." It spins its body like a propeller to swim.

STARYU
TYPE: Water
HEIGHT: 0.8m
WEIGHT: 34.5kg

Staryu's red core glows brightly in the dark. When it flashes this light, it is said to be communing with the stars.

STEELIX
TYPE: Steel - Ground
HEIGHT: 9.2m
WEIGHT: 400.0kg

Steelix lives deep underground and can tunnel straight down more than half a mile below the surface.

STOUTLAND
TYPE: Normal
HEIGHT: 1.2m
WEIGHT: 61.0kg

Stoutland excels at cold-weather rescues. Wrapped up in its warm, shaggy fur, someone could even spend the night on a snowy mountain and be OK.

STUNFISK
TYPE: Ground - Electric
HEIGHT: 0.7m
WEIGHT: 11.0kg

Stunfisk buries its flat body in mud, so it's hard to see and often gets stepped on. When that happens, its thick skin keeps it from being hurt, and it zaps the offender with a cheery smile.

STUNKY
TYPE: Poison - Dark
HEIGHT: 0.4m
WEIGHT: 19.2kg

The terrible-smelling fluid that Stunky sprays from its rear can keep others far away from it for a whole day.

SUDOWOODO
TYPE: Rock
HEIGHT: 1.2m
WEIGHT: 32.0kg

For most of the year, Sudowoodo can easily disguise itself as a tree for protection. However, in the winter, its green hands give it away.

LEGENDARY
SUICUNE
TYPE: Water
HEIGHT: 2.0m
WEIGHT: 187.0kg

Suicune can clear pollution from lakes and rivers. This Legendary Pokémon's heart is as pure as clear water.

SUNFLORA
TYPE: Grass
HEIGHT: 0.8m
WEIGHT: 8.5kg

Sunflora soaks up the sun's rays and transforms that energy into nutrients. It's very active during the warmth of the day, but when sunset arrives, it stops moving.

SUNKERN
TYPE: Grass
HEIGHT: 0.3m
WEIGHT: 1.8kg

Sunkern doesn't consume food but lives entirely on dewdrops. It avoids movement as much as possible so it doesn't use up its stored energy.

SURSKIT
TYPE: Bug - Water
HEIGHT: 0.5m
WEIGHT: 1.7kg

The point on Surskit's head produces a sweet syrup that attracts some Pokémon. The points on its feet give off an oil that lets it skate across the surface of the water.

SWABLU
TYPE: Normal - Flying
HEIGHT: 0.4m
WEIGHT: 1.2kg

Swablu uses its cottony wings to polish everything around it. It also likes to land on people's heads, so a woman walking down the sidewalk could suddenly discover she's wearing a fluffy Swablu hat.

SWADLOON
TYPE: Bug - Grass
HEIGHT: 0.5m
WEIGHT: 7.3kg

When many Swadloon live in a forest, the plants grow strong and healthy. These Pokémon eat fallen leaves and give off nutrients that enrich the soil.

SWALOT
TYPE: Poison
HEIGHT: 1.7m
WEIGHT: 80.0kg

Swalot's mouth can open wide enough to swallow a car tire easily. It defends itself by secreting a poisonous fluid.

SWAMPERT
TYPE: Water - Ground
HEIGHT: 1.5m
WEIGHT: 81.9kg

Swampert can tell when a storm is coming by shifts in the winds and waves. It's strong enough to drag and lift heavy boulders, so it builds a fort to take shelter.

SWANNA
TYPE: Water - Flying
HEIGHT: 1.3m
WEIGHT: 24.2kg

In the evening, a flock of Swanna performs an elegant dance around its leader. Their exceptional stamina and wing strength allow them to fly thousands of miles at a time.

SWELLOW
TYPE: Normal - Flying
HEIGHT: 0.7m
WEIGHT: 19.8kg

Soaring gracefully through the sky, Swellow will go into a steep dive if it spots food on the ground. It's very vain about keeping its wings properly groomed.

SWINUB
TYPE: Ice - Ground
HEIGHT: 0.4m
WEIGHT: 6.5kg

Swinub keeps its nose to the ground in search of food. Its favorite thing to eat is a certain kind of mushroom found under dead grass. Sometimes, it finds a hot spring while it's sniffing about.

SWIRLIX
TYPE: Fairy
HEIGHT: 0.4m
WEIGHT: 3.5kg

Swirlix loves to snack on sweets. Its sugary eating habits have made its white fur sweet and sticky, just like cotton candy.

SWOOBAT
TYPE: Psychic - Flying
HEIGHT: 0.9m
WEIGHT: 10.5kg

When a male Swoobat is trying to impress a female, it gives off ultrasonic waves that put everyone in a good mood. Under other circumstances, Swoobat's waves can pulverize concrete.

SYLVEON
TYPE: Fairy
HEIGHT: 1.0m
WEIGHT: 23.5kg

To keep others from fighting, Sylveon projects a calming aura from its feelers, which look like flowing ribbons. It wraps those ribbons around its Trainer's arm when they walk together.

TAILLOW
TYPE: Normal - Flying
HEIGHT: 0.3m
WEIGHT: 2.3kg

Although Taillow is fierce and courageous in battle, even against stronger foes, hunger or loneliness sometimes makes it cry.

TALONFLAME
TYPE: Fire - Flying
HEIGHT: 1.5m
WEIGHT: 24.5kg

Talonflame can swoop at incredible speeds when attacking. During intense battles, its wings give off showers of embers as it flies.

TANGELA
TYPE: Grass
HEIGHT: 1.0m
WEIGHT: 35.0kg

If grabbed by an attacker, Tangela can break away and leave the foe with a handful of vines. The vines grow back within a day.

TANGROWTH
TYPE: Grass
HEIGHT: 2.0m
WEIGHT: 128.6kg

During warmer times of the year, Tangrowth's vines grow so rapidly that they cover its eyes. It can control its vines like arms.

TAUROS
TYPE: Normal
HEIGHT: 1.4m
WEIGHT: 88.4kg

Tauros just isn't happy unless it's battling. If nobody's up for the challenge, it blows off steam by charging at trees and knocking them over.

TEDDIURSA
TYPE: Normal
HEIGHT: 0.6m
WEIGHT: 8.8kg

Teddiursa changes the flavor of its honey-soaked paws by incorporating different kinds of berries and pollen.

TENTACOOL
TYPE: Water - Poison
HEIGHT: 0.9m
WEIGHT: 45.5kg

If a Tentacool spends too much time out of water, its body will dry out. In the sea, it can focus and redirect sunlight into energy beams.

TENTACRUEL
TYPE: Water - Poison
HEIGHT: 1.6m
WEIGHT: 55.0kg

When the red orbs on Tentacruel's head glow, it's about to unleash a sonic blast that stirs up the sea. Its poisonous tentacles can extend to catch food.

TEPIG
TYPE: Fire
HEIGHT: 0.5m
WEIGHT: 9.9kg

Tepig uses the fireballs from its nose in battle–and in cooking! It likes to roast berries rather than eating them raw, though sometimes they get a little overdone.

LEGENDARY

TERRAKION
TYPE: Rock - Fighting
HEIGHT: 1.9m
WEIGHT: 260.0kg

Legends tell of a time when Terrakion attacked a mighty castle to protect its Pokémon friends. They say it knocked down a giant wall with the force of its charge

THROH
TYPE: Fighting
HEIGHT: 1.3m
WEIGHT: 55.5kg

Throh make belts for themselves out of vines and pull those belts tight to power up their muscles. They can't resist the challenge of throwing a bigger opponent

LEGENDARY

THUNDURUS
TYPE: Electric - Flying
HEIGHT: 1.5m
WEIGHT: 61.0kg

Thundurus can discharge powerful electric bolts from the spikes on its tail. This Legendary Pokémon causes terrible lightning storms, which often result in forest fires.

TIMBURR
TYPE: Fighting
HEIGHT: 0.6m
WEIGHT: 12.5kg

Timburr always carries a wooden beam, which it trades for bigger ones as it grows. These Pokémon can be a big help to construction workers.

TIRTOUGA
TYPE: Water - Rock
HEIGHT: 0.7m
WEIGHT: 16.5kg

Tirtouga is an excellent swimmer and diver, reaching depths of half a mile. It can also leave its ocean home to search for food on land. It was restored from a fossil.

TOGEKISS
TYPE: Fairy - Flying
HEIGHT: 1.5m
WEIGHT: 38.0kg

Togekiss flies around the world to seek out places of peace, bringing gifts and blessings to those who practice respect and harmony toward one another.

TOGEPI
TYPE: Fairy
HEIGHT: 0.3m
WEIGHT: 1.5kg

Togepi soaks up good vibes from other beings for use as energy. Its shell is filled with happy feelings and warm fuzzies.

TOGETIC
TYPE: Fairy - Flying
HEIGHT: 0.6m
WEIGHT: 3.2kg

Widely regarded as a bringer of good luck, Togetic seeks out people with pure hearts and showers happiness upon them.

TORCHIC
TYPE: Fire
HEIGHT: 0.4m
WEIGHT: 2.5kg

Torchic's internal fire and soft feathers make it a perfect cuddle buddy. In battle, it can breathe flames and shoot fireballs!

TORKOAL
TYPE: Fire
HEIGHT: 0.5m
WEIGHT: 80.4kg

Torkoal gets its energy by burning coal, which it digs up from mountains and uses to fill the hollow parts of its shell. The coal burns faster if it's fueling up for battle.

LEGENDARY

TORNADUS
TYPE: Flying
HEIGHT: 1.5m
WEIGHT: 63.0kg

Wrapped in its cloud, Tornadus flies at 200 mph. This Legendary Pokémon causes fierce windstorms with gales that can knock down houses.

TORTERRA
TYPE: Grass - Ground
HEIGHT: 2.2m
WEIGHT: 310.0kg

There's enough room on Torterra's enormous back for several small Pokémon to make their nests. According to ancient folklore, a particularly large one lived under the ground.

TOTODILE
TYPE: Water
HEIGHT: 0.6m
WEIGHT: 9.5kg

Be careful around a playful Totodile! It tends to nibble on friends as a sign of affection, but its jaws are strong enough to cause serious harm.

TOXICROAK
TYPE: Poison - Fighting
HEIGHT: 1.3m
WEIGHT: 44.4kg

Toxicroak's dangerous poison is stored in its throat sac and delivered through the claws on its knuckles.

TRANQUILL
TYPE: Normal - Flying
HEIGHT: 0.6m
WEIGHT: 15.0kg

Tranquill can always find its way back home, whether to its nest deep in the forest or to its Trainer's side. It's said that when these Pokémon nest together, peace surrounds the area.

TRAPINCH
TYPE: Ground
HEIGHT: 0.7m
WEIGHT: 15.0kg

Trapinch lives in the desert, where it can go without water for several days. It digs a bowl-shaped pit in the sand and hides at the bottom, waiting for something to fall in.

TREECKO
TYPE: Grass
HEIGHT: 0.5m
WEIGHT: 5.0kg

The tiny hooks on Treecko's feet allow it to climb straight up walls. With its calm attitude, it coolly stands up to bigger opponents.

TREVENANT
TYPE: Ghost - Grass
HEIGHT: 1.1m
WEIGHT: 71.0kg

Using its roots, Trevenant can control the trees around it to protect its forest home. Smaller Pokémon sometimes live in its hollow body.

TROPIUS
TYPE: Grass - Flying
HEIGHT: 2.0m
WEIGHT: 100.0kg

Tropius eats so much fruit that it started to grow its own fruit around its neck. The fruit is a popular snack for youngsters.

TRUBBISH
TYPE: Poison
HEIGHT: 0.6m
WEIGHT: 31.0kg

Trubbish live in grungy, germy, grimy places and release a gas that induces sleep in anyone who breathes it. They were created when household garbage reacted with chemical waste.

TURTWIG
TYPE: Grass
HEIGHT: 0.4m
WEIGHT: 10.2kg

Turtwig's shell is made of soil, and its whole body can produce energy via photosynthesis. If it goes too long without water, its leaf wilts.

TYMPOLE
TYPE: Water
HEIGHT: 0.5m
WEIGHT: 4.5kg

Tympole creates sound waves with the vibrations of its cheeks. People can't hear these sounds, so it can communicate with others undetected.

TYNAMO
TYPE: Electric
HEIGHT: 0.2m
WEIGHT: 0.3kg

A single Tynamo can't generate much power, but when several of them join forces, they can unleash an electric shock with the force of a lightning strike.

TYPHLOSION
TYPE: Fire
HEIGHT: 1.7m
WEIGHT: 79.5kg

The heat shimmer given off by Typhlosion's flames serves to conceal the Pokémon's movements. It can unleash a fiery explosion to scorch everything around it.

TYRANITAR
TYPE: Rock - Dark
HEIGHT: 2.0m
WEIGHT: 202.0kg

Tyranitar lives in the mountains, where it often goes wandering in search of battle opponents. It has been known to topple a mountain when building a nest.

TYRANTRUM
TYPE: Rock - Dragon
HEIGHT: 2.5m
WEIGHT: 270.0kg

Tyrantrum's enormous and powerful jaws made it the boss of its ancient world. Nothing could challenge its rule.

TYROGUE
TYPE: Fighting
HEIGHT: 0.7m
WEIGHT: 21.0kg

Training and working out every day is a must for keeping Tyrogue's stress levels under control. Its Trainer must take a disciplined approach.

TYRUNT
TYPE: Rock - Dragon
HEIGHT: 0.8m
WEIGHT: 26.0kg

Tyrunt often responds to frustration by pitching a fit. This ancient Pokémon lived millions of years ago.

UMBREON
TYPE: Dark
HEIGHT: 1.0m
WEIGHT: 27.0kg

When Umbreon springs into battle, the ring pattern in its fur begins to glow. The influence of moonlight caused it to evolve.

UNFEZANT
TYPE: Normal - Flying
HEIGHT: 1.2m
WEIGHT: 29.0kg

Unfezant has a prickly personality and rarely bonds with anyone other than its Trainer. The males have impressive head plumage, and the females are better at flying.

UNOWN
TYPE: Psychic
HEIGHT: 0.5m
WEIGHT: 5.0g

Unown can be found in many different shapes that resemble ancient writing. It's not known which came first.

URSARING
TYPE: Normal
HEIGHT: 1.8m
WEIGHT: 128.5kg

Ursaring makes daily rounds through the forest where it lives, climbing high into the trees and splashing through the streams to find food.

LEGENDARY

UXIE
TYPE: Psychic
HEIGHT: 0.3m
WEIGHT: 0.3kg

According to legend, Uxie brought the gift of intelligence to humankind. It is known as "The Being of Knowledge."

VANILLISH
TYPE: Ice
HEIGHT: 1.1m
WEIGHT: 41.0kg

Vanillish live in snow-covered mountains and battle using particles of ice they create by chilling the air around them.

VANILLITE
TYPE: Ice
HEIGHT: 0.4m
WEIGHT: 5.7kg

When the sun rose and cast its light on icicles, Vanillite were created. With their icy breath, they can surround themselves with snow showers.

VANILLUXE
TYPE: Ice
HEIGHT: 1.3m
WEIGHT: 57.5kg

From the water it gulps down, Vanilluxe creates snowy stormclouds inside its body. When it becomes angry, it uses those clouds to form a raging blizzard.

VAPOREON
TYPE: Water
HEIGHT: 10m
WEIGHT: 29.0kg

With its gills and fins, Vaporeon has adapted to an aquatic life. It can control its watery habitat with ease.

VENIPEDE
TYPE: Bug - Poison
HEIGHT: 0.4m
WEIGHT: 5.3kg

Venipede uses the feelers at both ends of its body to explore its surroundings. It's extremely aggressive, and its bite is poisonous.

VENOMOTH
TYPE: Bug - Poison
HEIGHT: 1.5m
WEIGHT: 12.5kg

When they become active after dark, Venomoth are often drawn to street lamps. It isn't the light that attracts them, but the promise of food.

VENONAT
TYPE: Bug - Poison
HEIGHT: 1.0m
WEIGHT: 30.0kg

Venonat's large, sensitive eyes pick up even the tiniest movement. The stiff hair that covers its body protects it from harm.

VENUSAUR
TYPE: Grass - Poison
HEIGHT: 2.0m
WEIGHT: 100.0kg

When Venusaur is well nourished and spends enough time in the sun, the flower on its back is brightly colored. The blossom gives off a soothing scent.

VESPIQUEN
TYPE: Bug - Flying
HEIGHT: 1.2m
WEIGHT: 38.5kg

Vespiquen controls the colony that lives in its honeycomb body by releasing pheromones. It feeds the colony with honey provided by Combee.

VIBRAVA
TYPE: Ground - Dragon
HEIGHT: 1.1m
WEIGHT: 15.3kg

Vibrava's wings aren't strong enough to fly very far, but it can vibrate them to produce ultrasonic waves that can give anyone listening a bad headache.

MYTHICAL

VICTINI
- **TYPE:** Psychic - Fire
- **HEIGHT:** 0.4m
- **WEIGHT:** 4.0kg

According to myth, Victini can bring victory in any kind of competition. Because it creates unlimited energy, it can share the overflow with others.

VICTREEBEL
- **TYPE:** Grass - Poison
- **HEIGHT:** 1.7m
- **WEIGHT:** 15.5kg

Victreebel uses its long vine like a fishing lure, swishing and flicking it to draw prey closer to its gaping mouth.

VIGOROTH
- **TYPE:** Normal
- **HEIGHT:** 1.4m
- **WEIGHT:** 46.5kg

Vigoroth just can't sit still! If it spends too much time inactive, it gets stressed out and goes on a rampage. It doesn't sleep very well.

VILEPLUME
- **TYPE:** Grass - Poison
- **HEIGHT:** 1.2m
- **WEIGHT:** 18.6kg

Many people are terribly allergic to the poisonous pollen Vileplume gives off. The petals of its flower are truly enormous.

LEGENDARY

VIRIZION
- **TYPE:** Grass - Fighting
- **HEIGHT:** 2.0m
- **WEIGHT:** 200.0kg

According to legend, Virizion can move so swiftly that its opponents are left bewildered. Its horns are lovely and graceful—and as sharp as blades.

VIVILLON
- **TYPE:** Bug - Flying
- **HEIGHT:** 1.2m
- **WEIGHT:** 17.0kg

The colorful patterns on Vivillon's wings are determined by the Pokémon's habitat. Vivillon from different parts of the world have different wing patterns.

VOLBEAT
- **TYPE:** Bug
- **HEIGHT:** 0.7m
- **WEIGHT:** 17.7kg

When night falls, Volbeat flashes the light on its tail in different patterns to send messages to others. It follows the sweet scent of Illumise.

MYTHICAL

VOLCANION
- **TYPE:** Fire - Water
- **HEIGHT:** 1.7m
- **WEIGHT:** 195.0kg

VOLCARONA
- **TYPE:** Bug - Fire
- **HEIGHT:** 1.6m
- **WEIGHT:** 46.0kg

The scales that cover Volcarona's six wings are like embers, and it scatters them to engulf the battlefield in flames. Its fire shines as bright as the sun.

VOLTORB
- **TYPE:** Electric
- **HEIGHT:** 0.5m
- **WEIGHT:** 10.4kg

Voltorb looks a lot like a Poké Ball, and it was first spotted at a Poké Ball factory. What's the connection? Nobody knows.

VULLABY
- **TYPE:** Dark - Flying
- **HEIGHT:** 0.5m
- **WEIGHT:** 9.0kg

Vullaby's wings aren't yet big enough to carry it through the air. The bones it wears around its lower half are gathered by Mandibuzz.

VULPIX
- **TYPE:** Fire
- **HEIGHT:** 0.6m
- **WEIGHT:** 9.9kg

Vulpix starts its life with a single tail that splits into six as it grows. The fire inside its body is constantly burning.

WAILMER
- **TYPE:** Water
- **HEIGHT:** 2.0m
- **WEIGHT:** 130.0kg

Wailmer is so round because it stores seawater inside its body. It can use this water to inflate itself for higher bounces, or shoot the water from its nostrils.

WAILORD
- **TYPE:** Water
- **HEIGHT:** 14.5m
- **WEIGHT:** 398.0kg

The enormous Wailord makes its home in the open sea, where it swims with its mouth open to gather food. Sometimes it leaps out of the water, crashing back down with a massive splash.

WALREIN
- **TYPE:** Ice - Water
- **HEIGHT:** 1.4m
- **WEIGHT:** 150.6kg

Walrein's giant tusks are capable of smashing through icebergs. Its thick blubber keeps it warm in frigid seas and is great for fending off hits in battle.

WARTORTLE
- **TYPE:** Water
- **HEIGHT:** 1.0m
- **WEIGHT:** 22.5kg

The fur on Wartortle's tail darkens with age. Its shell bears the scratches of many battles.

WATCHOG
- **TYPE:** Normal
- **HEIGHT:** 1.1m
- **WEIGHT:** 27.0kg

Watchog can make its stripes and eyes glow in the dark. Its tail stands straight up to alert others when it spots an intruder.

WEAVILE
- **TYPE:** Dark - Ice
- **HEIGHT:** 1.1m
- **WEIGHT:** 34.0kg

In the snowy places where they live, Weavile communicate with others in the area by leaving carvings in tree trunks. They work together to hunt for food.

WEEDLE
TYPE: Bug - Poison
HEIGHT: 0.3m
WEIGHT: 3.2kg

Weedle's sense of smell is excellent. With its large red nose, it can sniff out the leaves it likes best.

WEEPINBELL
TYPE: Grass - Poison
HEIGHT: 1.0m
WEIGHT: 6.4kg

The hooked stem behind its head lets Weepinbell hang from a tree branch to sleep. Sometimes it falls to the ground during the night.

WEEZING
TYPE: Poison
HEIGHT: 1.2m
WEIGHT: 9.5kg

Rotting food gives off a noxious gas that attracts Weezing. Its twin bodies take turns inflating and deflating to keep its poisonous gases churning.

WHIMSICOTT
TYPE: Grass - Fairy
HEIGHT: 0.7m
WEIGHT: 6.6kg

Where the winds whirl, Whimsicott appear, slipping into homes through the tiniest cracks and playing tricks on people. The white fluff they leave behind sometimes gives them away.

WHIRLIPEDE
TYPE: Bug - Poison
HEIGHT: 1.2m
WEIGHT: 58.5kg

Covered in a sturdy shell, Whirlipede doesn't move much unless it's attacked. Then it leaps into action, spinning at high velocity and smashing into the attacker.

WHISCASH
TYPE: Water - Ground
HEIGHT: 0.9m
WEIGHT: 23.6kg

If you get too close to a pond where a Whiscash lives, it might thrash so violently to protect its territory that it sets off an earthquake. It can also sense when a regular earthquake is coming.

WHISMUR
TYPE: Normal
HEIGHT: 0.6m
WEIGHT: 16.3kg

When Whismur isn't in trouble, the noises it makes are very quiet. As soon as danger approaches, it sounds an earsplitting wail.

WIGGLYTUFF
TYPE: Normal - Fairy
HEIGHT: 1.0m
WEIGHT: 12.0kg

A protective coating of tears covers Wigglytuff's enormous eyes, keeping the dust away. It can suck in air to inflate its flexible body until it resembles a balloon.

WINGULL
TYPE: Water - Flying
HEIGHT: 0.6m
WEIGHT: 9.5kg

With its long wings, Wingull can catch updrafts from the sea and glide across the sky as if on skates. It hides food and other treasures in various places.

WOBBUFFET
TYPE: Psychic
HEIGHT: 1.3m
WEIGHT: 28.5kg

Relying on its powers of endurance, Wobbuffet prefers not to attack—unless a foe goes after its tail. Then, it unleashes a powerful counterstrike.

WOOBAT
TYPE: Psychic - Flying
HEIGHT: 0.4m
WEIGHT: 2.1kg

When Woobat attaches itself to something, it leaves a heart-shaped mark with its nose. The nose is also the source of its echolocation signals.

WOOPER
TYPE: Water - Ground
HEIGHT: 0.4m
WEIGHT: 8.5kg

Though Wooper usually live in the water, they sometimes come ashore to look for food. To protect their bodies, they cover themselves with a sticky substance that is poisonous to the touch.

WORMADAM
TYPE: Bug - Grass
HEIGHT: 0.5m
WEIGHT: 6.5kg

The cloak it wore as Burmy becomes a permanent part of Wormadam's body. Its appearance is determined by its surroundings at the time of Evolution.

WURMPLE
TYPE: Bug
HEIGHT: 0.3m
WEIGHT: 3.6kg

With the spikes on its tail, Wurmple strips away tree back to get at the delicious sap underneath. The spikes also come in handy when fending off an attacker.

WYNAUT
TYPE: Psychic
HEIGHT: 0.6m
WEIGHT: 14.0kg

If a Wynaut is smacking its tail against the ground, that means it's angry, regardless of the big smile on its face.

XATU
TYPE: Psychic - Flying
HEIGHT: 1.5m
WEIGHT: 15.0kg

Some people believe Xatu can see the future, and they respect its mystical powers. When it stands still for hours on end, they say it's petrified by terrible visions.

LEGENDARY

XERNEAS
TYPE: Fairy
HEIGHT: 3.0m
WEIGHT: 215.0kg

Xerneas's horns shine in all the colors of the rainbow. It is said that this Legendary Pokémon can share the gift of endless life.

YAMASK
TYPE: Ghost
HEIGHT: 0.5m
WEIGHT: 1.5kg

The mask that Yamask carries is said to represent its face from a former life. Sometimes, remembering that former life makes it very sad.

YANMA
TYPE: Bug - Flying
HEIGHT: 1.2m
WEIGHT: 38.0kg

With its compound eyes, Yanma can see in every direction without moving its head. It can make quick stops and turns during flight.

YANMEGA
TYPE: Bug - Flying
HEIGHT: 1.9m
WEIGHT: 51.5kg

With four wings on its back and two more on its tail to keep it balanced, Yanmega is capable of extremely high-speed flight. It can carry a full-grown person through the air.

LEGENDARY
YVELTAL
TYPE: Dark - Flying
HEIGHT: 5.8m
WEIGHT: 203.0kg

When Yveltal spreads its dark wings, its feathers give off a red glow. It is said that this Legendary Pokémon can absorb the life energy of others.

ZANGOOSE
TYPE: Normal
HEIGHT: 1.3m
WEIGHT: 40.3kg

Zangoose slashes at opponents with its sharp claws extended. These Pokémon constantly feud with Seviper.

LEGENDARY
ZAPDOS
TYPE: Electric - Flying
HEIGHT: 1.6m
WEIGHT: 52.6kg

When Zapdos is hit by a bolt of lightning, its power increases. This Legendary Pokémon can bend electricity to its will.

ZEBSTRIKA
TYPE: Electric
HEIGHT: 1.6m
WEIGHT: 79.5kg

A herd of Zebstrika running at top speed gives off a noise like thunder. If they get angry, their manes shoot off lightning.

ZIGZAGOON
TYPE: Normal
HEIGHT: 0.4m
WEIGHT: 17.5kg

Zigzagoon's curiosity drives it to wander constantly and restlessly. It rubs the sturdy bristles on its back against trees to mark its territory.

LEGENDARY
ZEKROM
TYPE: Dragon - Electric
HEIGHT: 2.9m
WEIGHT: 354.0kg

Legends say Zekrom helps those who pursue their ideals. It surrounds itself with thunderclouds to travel unseen, and its tail can generate electricity.

ZORUA
TYPE: Dark
HEIGHT: 0.7m
WEIGHT: 12.5kg

Zorua can use the power of illusion to make itself look like a person or a different Pokémon. It sometimes uses the resulting confusion to flee from a battle.

ZOROARK
TYPE: Dark
HEIGHT: 1.6m
WEIGHT: 81.1kg

Masters of deception, Zoroark are able to create entire landscapes out of illusions. In this way, they can scare or trick people away from their territory and protect their pack.

ZUBAT
TYPE: Poison - Flying
HEIGHT: 0.8m
WEIGHT: 7.5kg

Sunlight isn't good for Zubat, so it stays hidden during the day. It prefers dark places like caves and old houses.

ZWEILOUS
TYPE: Dark - Dragon
HEIGHT: 1.4m
WEIGHT: 50.0kg

Zweilous has a ravenous appetite and exhausts the local food supply before moving on. Rather than working together, its two heads compete for food.

LEGENDARY
ZYGARDE
TYPE: Dragon - Ground
HEIGHT: 5.0m
WEIGHT: 305.0kg

Zygarde dwells deep within a cave in the Kalos region. It is said that this Legendary Pokémon is a guardian of the ecosystem.

ANSWERS

Pokémon Quiz - Part 1 (Pages 12 and 13)
`A Meeting of Two Journeys!`

1=C, 2=A, 3=C, 4=B, 5=A, 6=C, 7=A, 8=C, 9=B, 10=C

Pokémon Scramble! (Page 14)

Bonnie, Sceptile, Nurse Joy, Meowth, Lysandre, Xerosic, Inkay, special Pokémon = Pikachu

Pokémon Sudoku (Page 15)

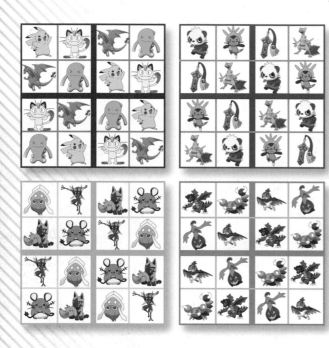

Thunderbolt Code (Pages 16 and 17)

WHEN MANY PIKACHU GATHER THEIR ELECTRICITY CAN BUILD AND CAN CAUSE LIGHTNING STORMS

Pokémon Quiz - Part 2 (Pages 24 and 25)
`An Explosive Operation!`

1=B, 2=C, 3=A, 4=B, 5=A, 6=A, 7=C, 8=B, 9=C, 10=A

Criss Cross Pokémon (Page 26)

Poké Ball Search (Page 27)

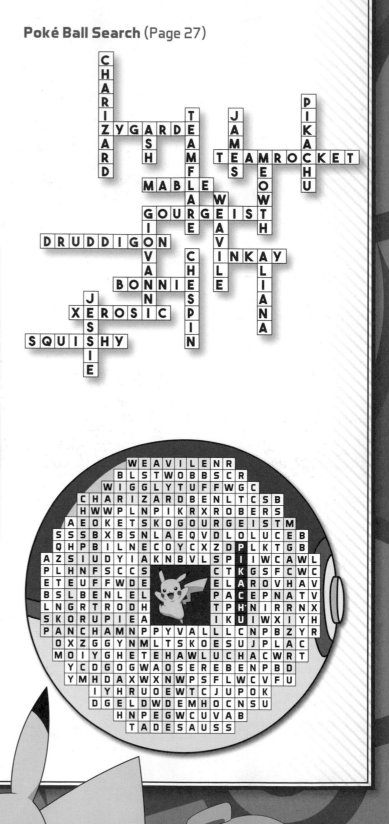